Solas

[sol-uhz]

noun **(Scottish Gaelic)**

1. Light.

'An **solas** san dorchadas.'

('The light in the darkness.')

Solace

[**sol**-is]

noun **(English)**

1. Comfort or consolation in a time of distress or sadness.

"The written word provides **solace** in times of strife."

Solas

This paperback edition was first published 2022 by Stryvling Press
University of Stirling, Stirling, Scotland FK9 4LA
https://stryvlingpress.stir.ac.uk/

ISBN: 978-1-908063-57-1

Cover Images: Ella Gallego and Jane Armstrong
Motifs: Jane Armstrong
Scottish Gaelic Language Advisor: Joe Sanders
Typeset in Garamond Premiere Pro

Printed and bound by:
Bell & Bain Ltd.
303 Burnfield Road
Thornliebank
Glasgow
G46 7UQ

❧ 5 YEARS OF LITERARY EXCELLENCE

Also available from

STRYVLING PRESS

Pharos
Circling the Point
Time and Tide
Inklings

2022

Foreword

──*Dr. Liam Bell*──

This anthology is the fifth collaboration between the Creative Writing and Publishing Studies courses here at the University of Stirling, but it also marks a significant first. This is our first 'double cohort' of writers on the MLitt; with our 2020 intake delayed by the pandemic and our 2021 intake arriving hot on their heels. That has created a unique set of challenges for the writers in this volume, from dealing with online classes to trying to navigate self-isolation and testing regimes. It is testament to them that they have managed to foster a sense of community and camaraderie throughout, with friendships burgeoning both in the classroom and through online spaces.

I will remember them for the care with which they approached workshops. Whether on a screen or in a room, they have been supportive of one another and created an environment in which each and every writer has grown and developed hugely. There are those who continued on from undergraduate studies and went on to greater heights; those who have returned to university and brought expertise (and story material) from the world of work; and there are our US students who have embraced life in Scotland with warmth and generosity of spirit.

To have simply progressed through the course, under the circumstances of the last two years, would be an achievement, but the writers on display here have done so much more, as you will see. These are authors who are fully attentive to their writing and to the world around them, creating imaginative worlds and keenly observed characters. There is a lively engagement with genre and with form, there are immersive voices which will linger with you long after reading.

It has been a pleasure to have them with us, developing their craft, and we also owe a debt of gratitude to the superb Stryvling team for all their hard work in producing such a beautiful publication. It is a collection of immense quality and one which positively thrums with the promise of more to come from all these wonderfully talented folk. The writers here are only taking their first steps in the industry but, mark my words, they will travel far...

Table of Contents

—*WINTER*—

WINTER

WINTER

Today I Am

—Jennifer Syme—

Feeling foggy of head,
And the words won't come
To my mind.

(Today I am)
Frustrated with this
Claustrophobia in my brain
And my thoughts imprisoned
By invisible bars.

(Today I am)
Angry with the fog,
The block, and this restricted life, so
Far away from my true self.

(Today I am)
Hopeful, that one day
Those words will flow.
When the fog has gone, and
The cage dissolved.
I will look forward to
The new life that
Is waiting for me and
Those words now free to fly.

plunder of a trespasser

—— Hayli McClain ——

trespassing was invented
      after i grew up
before that, property lines were
      playground equipment
how many could i hurdle?
      and wonder if i can super-spy-slip
unharmed between the humming wires
      of the horse lady's electric fence?

catchin' crawdads in the crick
      barefoot under the bridge
shhrrmmm shhrrmmm would go the cars
      of POSTED-sign neighbours overhead
come sunset i'd slosh home a bucket of silty plunder
      and ask dad is it okay
if i keep my new pets
      in that dusty fish tank downstairs?
sure, he'd say, *but just for the weekend—*
      they deserve to be free.

Night Walk in a Scots Pine Forest

——Marianne L. Berghuis——

The
hairs on
the back of
my neck stand
up. Eyes alert, body
m o t i o n l e s s.
My right hand rests upon
knotted, splintered tree bark.
Chilled evening air surrounds me.
My heart beats faster. The rhythm,
thump, thump, thump, drums in my ears.
Cutting wind wails through the branches. A twig
snaps. My breath quickens. The moon casts strange
lurching limb shadows from the swaying Scots pines.
Fumbling with my torch, my palms sweat. In the dull light,
a ghostly silence lurks. My gut flips and churns. Forked jagged prongs
appear before me. My panicked pupils dilate. Blood rushes to my leg muscles.
I am ready to run.
Crack, creak, crunch.
Two eyes meet mine.
I hold my breath.
Mighty midnight stag.

The Flat-Peak Baseball Cap

——Marianne L. Berghuis——

YOU SIT POISED AND WAIT patiently on the corner of the bedside table. You know that the bony fingers of an outstretched weak, skeletal arm will soon reach out for you. You are more than a fashion statement. Now, you provide protection for a once well-haired head. Your wide, flat-peak shades dulled youthful eyes. You are a baseball cap of camouflage green.

You were always important to him, but in this essential new role you are ready and willing to serve. You were there as his soft, brown hair started to fall out. Strand by strand. Clump by clump. You witnessed sleepless nights as he lay on a pillowcase covered with lost, loved locks. You were there when the itching started and anger and grief grew. You were there when he braved a blade-to-skin head shave and his patchy baldness was satisfyingly no more.

You are like armour on a battlefield for his every waking hour. You are a reminder of good times and symbolise hope for those times to come again.

He wakes. Your eleven year old. His body slowly rises and bit by bit he puts on his underwear, socks, grey joggy bottoms, and oversized marbled-black t-shirt. You remain patient. He stands, supporting himself on the back of a nearby chair. He glances into a full-length mirror on the wall, but he does not recognise what he sees. He turns his frail, pale body then reaches back to his bedside table. He depends on the comfort of your camouflage green.

Your wait is over. You are placed perfectly onto his smooth bald head. The wide brim of your flat-peak disguises his missing eyelashes and absent eyebrows.

With your help, a smile appears on his thin face. He is ready. Ready, with you, to face this brand-new day.

The Bench

—Marianne L. Berghuis—

(Looking out from a hospital window.)

TWO LOVERS CARESS. SITTING FACE to face. The sun shines into the eyes of the tall one as they raise a hand to block its blinding brightness. The lovers' knees slot together. Their toes touch and rest on the asphalt path. An arm moves around the tall one's shoulder and the short one leans in for a kiss. The sun-blocking arm is now redundant, so it stretches out and pulls the short one closer. A lingering kiss. The tall one comes up for air. The short one burrows their head into the curved gap between the tall one's neck and shoulder. The lovers' arms are wrapped tightly around each other, like ivy cloaked around an oak. Warmed by their embrace, their eyes close. I close mine too and visualise my husband's arms s t r e t c h i n g out to wrap around me.

Three boys sit huddled in a row. They are wearing black hoodies and jeans. The only distinction is coloured baseball caps. The flat peak ones, not the ones with the curved brim. They look too big for the boys' heads. One cap is camouflage coloured. One cap is red with a gold shiny logo, it glimmers as the sun catches it. The third blue cap now lies on the ground. Knocked off by one of the other boys. Its owner doesn't look too happy. He stands and gestures erratically with his hands while the others laugh. Their attention turns to the pizza boxes that camo-cap is holding. Dealt out, they sit. The box lids are flipped open. It looks like they haven't eaten in days. I salivate thinking about tomato, mushroom, pepper, pineapple, and cheese topped slices.

A dog walker passes. A salt and pepper schnauzer, heavy on the pepper, enthusiastically scampers. Nose alert, sniffing. The dog cocks its leg and relieves itself against a broad-leaved sycamore tree. The walker pauses. Something catches his eye, and he turns. He heads towards the bench. Schnauzer beats him there and sniffs ravenously at the cardboard. The walker picks up the discarded boxes and changes his direction towards a waste bin. He squashes the boxes with his heavy boots, then squeezes them into the bin's small oval gap. The dog is now at his owner's side. He kneels and strokes its head. Its tail is wagging, and its tongue is out panting. I sense the smoothness of stroking the dog's silky folded, floppy ears.

A cyclist slows. His left cleat adjusts swiftly to detach from its clipped pedal. Brakes are squeezed and the cyclist stops. He stretches his left foot out and supports himself on the bench. He removes his water bottle from its cradle attached to the bike frame. His spine arches backwards as he gulps down fluid from a striped, purple bottle. It's a contrast to the mud splattered yellow frame of his *'Specialized'* road bike. His face is red under the sleek air-vented helmet. His snug, moisture wicking cycling gear is darkened in patches by perspiration. He replaces the bottle securely into its cage. Then pushing off from the bench, he glides for a second as his foot clips back in. The pedals rotate. I imagine the clank and click as the gears shift.

Birdsong now faded.
Evening's darkened sky drifts in.
The bench rests alone.

As do I.

Labyrinth

——*Marianne L. Berghuis*——

WE'VE BEEN HALLOWEEN DAFT SINCE high school and tonight is our yearly meet-up. I turn on my Bluetooth speaker and Fields of the Nephilim's haunting vocals fill my small flat as I try to ignore a churning feeling in my stomach. I glance out the window. The full moon shines down on a grim reaper and werewolf skipping stupidly towards my front door. Smiling, I slug back the glass of bright green alcohol in my hand and open the door dressed as a skeleton bride. I invite John and Ann in. Drinks flowing, we all start prancing about in our costumes. John flicks my Spotify playlist to Bauhaus as we apply the finishing touches to our face paint. Downing the last dregs of cheap fortified wine, we grab torches from my hall unit and step out into the cold air. I notice a strange glow reflecting onto the street from the flickering street lights and my guts turn again.

The large maize labyrinth is an annual event. Costume-clad people mill about, warming themselves up by the hot chocolate stalls. It's already late and families with younger children are heading home. Two blazing braziers radiate heat from either side of the labyrinth entrance. The wavering corn stalks tower above John's six-foot-tall body. They cast menacing shadows as we approach. A green-wigged killer clown collects our tickets and directs us into the maze with a white gloved hand.

'I hate clowns,' John says.

The three of us link arms and enter. The clown's head turns, and its bloodshot eyes follow us in.

'Think Chainsaw-Guy is here?' Ann asks. 'He freaks me out.'

'It's Ghostface jumping out from nowhere that gets me,' I reply.

Wispy, shapeless clouds drift over the moon and the labyrinth darkens as we get deeper into the maze. Clinging couples and groups of screaming teenagers push past us. Ann trips and slices her finger on a sharp dried maize sheath.

'Ooh … they'll smell your blood,' jokes John.

A thunderous noise revs up behind us. Brrrrm … brrrm … brrrm.

'Fuck! I hate this,' I shriek. 'Why the hell do we do this again?'

Our hands separate. We all run. John stumbles into three hysterical girls and falls. Chainsaw-Guy leaps over him.

'A' right doon there, Wolfie?' he yells manically as he fleets past to follow the frenzied screams.

I offer out my hand and help John up.

'Where's Ann?' he asks.

I look round and shrug my shoulders. The path splits so we take the fork that is not filled by the girls screams. The path soon forks again.

'Shit, I must've dropped my torch,' John mutters. 'Stay here.'

I shiver and wait for John to return. Hairs on the back on my neck rise. *Am I being watched?* It's only actors, I tell myself. My torchlight has an eerie glow in the darkness.

'John?' I shout, 'Ann?'

No answer. I call again. Nothing. I turn and walk back the way I came. The path is now a dead end. Disorientated, I freeze on the spot. My heart is pounding, and my throat feels dry. I can't hear anything, not even the group of girls. The battery in my torch is fading, so I shuffle forwards with outstretched arms to feel my way. I get goosebumps. *Is someone behind me?*

'John? Ann? This ain't funny.'

A breeze ruffles at the back of my neck. I turn. Nobody is there. I catch something with my foot and shine the last dim light from my torch downwards. Ann's grim reaper scythe! A red trail disappears into the undergrowth. I shudder deep into my skeleton bride bones.

'Ann … Ann … what the actual fuck?' I scream.

I run, scraping my arms on the rough stalks of maize. The netted fabric of my costume snags and rips. My breathing quickens as bodyless footsteps crunch behind me. The feeling I've had lingering in my guts all night returns. I gag as bile rises into the back of my throat. I stagger forwards. My arm is grabbed, and I'm dragged between the maize stalks. I feel a hand placed firmly over my mouth.

It's John. He is shaking. He raises an index finger to his lips as he stares at me with tear-stained eyes.

'Ann's dead,' he gulps. 'Chainsaw-guy's gone freaking crazy.'

We stand motionless as the deafening shrill gets closer. Brrrrm … brrrm … brrrm.

You used to be Mabel

——Trish Stafanovic——

'You used to be Mabel
Incredibly able
Perfect and stable
That kind of Mabel.

Not someone who bores
Spending time mopping floors.'
Not answering doors
Hiding my sores
While anxiety gnaws.

When he laughs I don't mind
I turn my ears blind
He's cruel to be kind
I don't seek I don't find.

If I were a book, I would be a fable
A piece of furniture - a wobbly table
'A mental illness, you just need a label.
Snap out of the slump, you used to be Mable.'

He says, *'God loves a trier.'*
But I think he's a liar
I need to be slyer
To avoid his hell fire
His holy trip wire
Keep my arse from his mire.

'I know just how you feel
Take the pills you will heal.'
I nod along to his spiel
But my skin starts to peel
Unaware of the deal.

'What happened?' he says
From our separate beds.
It's hard to explain, why I'm unstable
'You used to be Mabel
Incredibly able.'

The voices they said
The ones in my head
That Mable is dead.

Wolf Tongue

—Trish Stefanovic—

SISTER PLACED THE WOLF ON the table. A dark, penned outline of a creature with an oversized head. His fat tongue rolled out like a sly welcome mat. His one eye fixed the children warily.

Angela heard him say, 'I am not yet in my full power. Trust me.'

Once painted he would be hung on the classroom wall next to the crucified Jesus, whose watchful gaze saw all Sister's daily cruelties.

'Paint carefully within the lines!' Sister screeched. 'Only use the grey paint. Only grey, no other colours.' Her voice rose, seeking out their stupid ears. 'Gather round the Wolf, quickly.'

She grabbed their shoulders and moved them firmly into casual positions. Happy children at group work, ready for Holy Father. Angela was at the Wolf's head. He looked directly at her.

'What will you make of me?' she heard him say.

'Do not paint the eye or tongue,' Sister commanded. 'Do you understand?'

'Yes, Sister.' They chorused, but not Angela.

'Grey paint only and stay between the lines.'

'Yes, Sister.'

Sister watched the door and waited for Holy Father to come.

Angela stared down at the badly drawn creature. You, Wolf, could not eat an old lady or make yourself a grandma and gobble the girl in the red cloak. The Wolf shook his head. 'No, not I.'

13

'Now. Start now,' Sister hissed. The classroom door opened, and she welcomed Holy Father. The children began to paint carefully between the lines. Sister cooed encouragement in a borrowed voice they had not heard before.

'They're painting the Wolf from Little Red Riding Hood,' she gushed.

'Blessed be!' said Father. 'Which part of the story do you like best?'

'When he eats them and makes their blood go everywhere,' Angela said.

The Wolf looked at her. His blank tongue hung slackly from his toothless mouth.

'Do it,' he said. 'You want to.'

Can't, she thought.

'Now,' he said.

I will, she thought.

She pushed her brush into the forbidden red paint and fed him a rich, slick, smear. His hungry tongue drooled wetly. She dripped blood red dollops into his gaping mouth. His hot breath warmed her face.

She heard Sister gasp, but Angela did not stop. The Wolf stirred under her defiant hands.

'More,' he growled.

Angela forgot the words and the warnings. She splattered her red all over him. The wolf began to lick, to move fast and fierce in bold blurs.

'Yes, Wolf,' she said.

'More,' he panted. 'Let me watch.'

She obeyed the Wolf, dipping her brush into the ice-cold blue and pushing it into his empty eye.

The wolf snarled. 'All - the - better - to - see - _you_ - with.'

The blue spilt out of his eye and into the red. He was wild, crazed, night-dark, a bloodshot swirl of pure bad Wolf. Angela laughed with joy.

Sister swooped down on her. 'Stop it, stop it!' she screamed.

'Eat me, Wolf, gobble me up,' Angela cried.

'Stop it. Stop it.' Sister shook Angela by the shoulders. She raised her hand high and slapped her hard across the face.

Later, when the paint was cleared away, Holy Father told the class Sister had gone, and she would not be coming back.

Angela looked at the Wolf, now high up on the wall, his watchful gaze seeing her, seeing all. He winked from his blue-blood eye. Fresh red drooled from his wet tongue. She smiled. She knew.

February 25th, 2022

—— Morgan MacVaugh ——

1,890 MILES AWAY, THE WORLD is ending, but here the sky is blue.

My love and I stroll through East Prince's Street Gardens, my hand tucked into the crook of her arm. White and purple blooms peek out on the hill below the monument. A dog gallops by in the lower stretch of grass, haunches wriggling. A woman with a pensive face says something quiet into a phone. I can't place the language.

A hundred people pass on this soft-boiled day, coaxed out by sunlight in winter.

From above the gallery, echoing in the station tunnels, a sound cracks across the city—stone off stone off stone. A hundred people pause together. My hand tightens around my love's arm. Together, our eyes part and meet across the space between us. I whisper, *Was that—?* She shakes her head, thinks for a moment. I see her heartbeat in her neck. We watch the sky. *The cannons*, she breathes, at last. *It's one o'clock*. Her eyes are manic. The dog has its head cocked. The woman sobs once into her phone.

We walk on.

The silence is collective, tangible, carried from person to person to person. I wonder if we all feel guilty, standing in the sun of an every-other day. A world away, the sun bleeds shells and sirens are going. I know I am guilty, because I will sleep through the night tonight.

1,890 miles away, the world is ending, but here—undeservedly—the sky is blue.

A Day's Difference

—*Ashleigh Marie Symms*—

Yesterday,
two drowsy Jack Russell Terriers
lay either side of her lap.
The cream corduroy couch
their bed for the night.
Heads rested softly
on used-to-be red tartan thighs.
Her pyjamas were covered
in layers of white, wiry fur.
Flickering flames warmed the room,
as the popping of the fire
sent them softly to sleep.

Today,
two cold, oak caskets
lie on the coffee table.
The freshly polished, gold brass plaques,
newly engraved.
Sitting upright and rigid
on the couch, she's inspecting
the long, bristly hairs,
threaded into her tartan pyjamas.
She cradles their blanket, inhaling

a mixture of sweet sweat, stale urine,

and the fox muck they used to roll in when out in the garden.

A Fresh Scratch

——*Ashleigh Marie Symms*——

YOU POUR YOUR FIRST GLASS of red. It's a merlot. French, you believe. You're standing in the kitchen next to the hob, boiling broccoli to go with the chicken that's roasting in the oven. You'll remove some of the florets when they're done blanching, ready for freezing. There's always too much for two when you buy it fresh.

Picking up the bottle by its neck, you bring it closer to your face. You don't remember where you've put your glasses, but they're not on your head. The label at the back reads: 'A Bordeaux blend with bold notes of ripened black currant and plum, and a distinct aroma of earthiness'. Nice, you think, but you don't understand all that. It looks fancy, almost certainly worth over £10. The sort of bottle you browse over in *Tesco*. You didn't buy it, wouldn't spend more than £5, £6 max, on a bottle. Well, you wouldn't because you aren't allowed. 'No point wasting extra pennies on wine when you drink it that fast,' he says.

You lift your glass and take a swig. It feels smooth as it runs down your throat. You sniff the wine before sitting the glass down again. It smells nothing like soil.

Water is frothing from the pan and spilling onto the cooker, sizzling as it touches the heat. Fuck, you've zoned out. The broccoli is done. You turn the hob off, cover the pan and set them to one side. You aren't cooking potatoes. Last time, he called you a stupid bitch for cooking carbs on a rest day. You didn't keep up with his workout schedule.

You turn the bottle around to see the front label. The glass scrapes along the speckled black, laminate counter. You wince at the noise, not quite as high-pitched as a screech, yet still enough to make your teeth throb and feel loose as if they'll fall out of your mouth at any second. A fresh scratch appears on the gloss finish of the

19

worktop. Shit. You lick your thumb and rub at it, pushing hard and hoping your spit will work like a magic eraser and simply wipe the damage away. It doesn't. Maybe he won't notice. It is next to the other three, deep scratches – that he had made cutting cheese without a chopping board – now engrained with food remnants. You think about squishing some broccoli over the new one to make it blend in. But no, you leave it.

The writing on the wine bottle is bigger on the front. 'Medium-bodied', you read without squinting. Good, you think, you can have more than one glass. One or two is the limit, he says. You remind yourself today is different. You *need* a drink; you don't just want one. You finish the last of your first glass and pour a second.

You spent the morning trying to finish what he started last night when he wrapped your long, auburn hair around your neck until you couldn't breathe. He held you as you flailed your arms, and your face went red, and your lips turned blue. Then, he let go. You dropped to the floor. And that's where he left you, gasping and sobbing, while he went to bed. You spent the night inhaling bits of dust, and what you hoped were only his chest hairs, from along the skirting, and listened to him snoring contently. So today, after he left for work, when the bathroom mirror revealed the perfect, purple choker he gifted to you, you took your hairdryer and wrapped the wire tightly around your neck until you felt your eyes straining. There was nowhere to hang from in your flat. You thought about cutting, but you couldn't muster the courage and there wasn't enough ibuprofen in the medicine cupboard for an overdose. When your arms weren't strong enough to send you to sleep, you did the only other thing you knew how to. You spent the afternoon painting on your mask.

Now, it's quite the picture. Subtle winged eyeliner, false lashes, red lip. Your skills were honed from learning how to hide the marks no one else should see.

You like this version of yourself. She smiles, dotes, and bites her tongue when she's supposed to, so you bring her out for the evenings, ready for his return from work.

You glance at the clock on the wall, gulp down the rest of your second glass of wine and pour your third. You have time.

The key turns in the lock. You hear the front door open, and bang shut. He's here. Bending down to check on the chicken, you practice your smiles in the glass of the oven door.

'Hello, Darling,' you say, as he rounds the corner into the kitchen. You force the words out of your mouth.

He ignores you and heads straight for the fridge.

'Dinner won't be long,' you tell him. You step closer and place a hand gently on his shoulder. The game is easier when you play on his side.

He shrugs your hand off and sighs. You catch a whiff of lager on his breath. You know what this means. He finished early and headed straight to the pub.

You stare at him as he opens the fridge. The anger burns behind your eyes. You want to scream. To tell him he's a selfish bastard. Tell him that you've spent all afternoon prepping his evening meal. By the time dinner is ready, you're never hungry. It's all for him. Your fingertips reek of garlic, and the smell makes you nauseous every time you put your hands near your face. He doesn't care.

You turn around and take a deep breath. Then you pick up your glass and drink, listening to him snorting in-between stuffing handfuls of – what you can only assume is – the honey-roast ham for his lunch tomorrow into his mouth. You wonder what the hell you'll put on his sandwiches now.

The popping of the cap off his beer snaps you out of your thoughts. He slams the fridge closed, rattling the milk bottles, raspberry jam, and jars of other sauces that live in the compartments in the fridge door. You jump. Wine sloshes over the rim of your glass, but you quickly steady your hand and try to only lose a few drops. But more than half the glass is gone now. You don't remember drinking that much.

It splashes onto the cream ceramic tiles, colouring the floor. Before he can huff, or grunt, or spit, you grab the sponge from the sink and squat down, wiping up the mess. When you look up, he's glaring at you.

In what he calls his 'calm voice', he says, 'Why didn't you put more lager in the fridge?'

It wasn't 'calm', it was just quieter than usual.

'Did I not do that? I'm sorry, I thought I did,' you say. You stand up now and get two plates out of the cupboard. Better to just get on with the dinner, you think.

'Why would I waste my breath asking you that question if they were in the fridge? You really are a fucking stupid bitch sometimes.'

He laughs as if it were a joke. Yes, you are, you think. You know better than that by now. But you don't admit it.

You smile and say, 'Sorry, darling, I'll do it now.'

'Don't bother, I'll do it my-fucking-self since you're busy getting pissed again on my money. You should stop fucking wasting the wine by spilling it all over the floor though.'

Shit, you thought you'd escaped that dig.

He begins lifting bottles of *Staropramen* out of their cardboard box on top of the fridge. The bottles clink against each other as he heavy-handedly shoves them in the fridge.

You pick up your wine and finish the last of it in one large mouthful. Then, slipping your oven gloves onto your hands, you lift the chicken out and onto the top of the hob to rest. You read online that it is best to let the meat rest before you carve it. It gives it time to soak up all the juices, or something like that. You pour the last of the wine into your glass, making it your fourth, and place the empty bottle on the counter above the bin. You'll take it outside to the glass bin later.

The fridge door shuts again, but he doesn't say anything. You find the silence eerie and turn to check if he is still in the room. He stands there, eyes darting from you to the now-empty merlot bottle on the side. His nostrils are already starting to flare.

'Where did you get that from?'

'It was in the cupboard,' you reply.

'Did I EVER once say that was for you?' Spit flies from his lips. You follow the droplet with your eyes as it falls to the floor.

'No, but I just assumed, it —'

'EXACTLY! You just assumed. And what happens when you assume?'

You stare at him. You know you need to pick your next words carefully.

'Well, I'll FUCKING TELL YOU, SHALL I?' He walks towards you and stops when he is as close as he can get without touching you.

'You make an ass out of you,' he says quietly. 'That bottle was for my Mum's birthday. What do you think you're doing fucking helping yourself?'

'You make an ass out of you and me,' you reply. You regret speaking.

'What did you just fucking say to me?'

'Sorry, no, nothing. I was just correcting you, well the saying. The saying is when you assume you make an ass out of you and me.'

'EXACTLY HOW I HAVE MADE AN ASS OUT OF MYSELF?' he booms.

Before you can reply, his hand connects with your cheek.

When you were little, seven or eight to be exact, your dad told you that men should never hit women. One day, when he was picking you up from school, he saw a boy push you over, laugh, and run away. He picked you up, brushed the gravel from your grazed knee, and told you never to let another little git hurt you ever again.

'Boys do not hit girls,' he said.

You asked, 'What if a girl hits a boy?'

He replied, 'Not even then.'

But your dad doesn't know what you were really like.

Nathan wasn't like the other men you've been with. Firstly, he didn't like being called by his name. He said pet names showed you loved him more. But he only responded to 'Darling'. He wasn't your husband, but he called you his 'Missus'. You used to like this. It gave you somewhere to belong. He wasn't ashamed to show you off. But after that first time, the first time he 'smacked some sense into you', you understood why he called you that. He owned you. And he wanted everyone else to know that too.

That was a year ago. You forgave him, of course. It was a mistake. You deserved it. You should never have finished that bottle of Australian Shiraz. But you did. The whole 75cl. And just like the wine, you became a little spicy as you felt your cheeks growing rosier. You thought *you* were robust, strong like the flavours of the berries and plums that made up the wine. You grew cocky, goaded him. You were clever like that. You told him you could have anyone you wanted. He was lucky to have you. You threatened him. You said you'd leave if he didn't start treating you right. But you pushed him too far. The first punch was a hard mouthful to swallow.

Nothing was the same after that. Once he knew you were forgiving, it became part of your routine. He took everything out on you. If he had a bad day at work, that was your fault. If someone cut him off when he was driving, that was your fault. If the batteries in the TV remote died, that was also your fault. You were bolshy to begin with. Shouted, screamed, wished he was dead. But you could never leave. Where would you go? Your dad was gone. There's nobody else. He'd freeze the bank account to stop you from accessing the money. That's why you were only allowed to take cash when shopping. He knew you would run. Or maybe you wouldn't, but he would never give you the opportunity to find out.

You once threw your boot straight at his head after he told you he didn't want you to wear them. But after the bruised rib and two broken fingers that you got from 'falling down' the communal stairs in the hallway, you learnt to keep your mouth shut.

You didn't stop thinking, though. At night, while you lay in bed, you would think about all the ways you could get rid of him for good. A pillow over his head. Poison in his food. Lock all the windows and doors before starting a fire. Knife to the throat. Hit him over the head with the empty glass vase on the windowsill. You were never allowed to put flowers in it anyway. It set off his hay fever. It would be good to get some use out of it.

But it didn't matter how many ideas you came up with, you weren't strong enough.

You raise your hand to your face. Your lip stings as you touch it, and you feel something warm and wet on your fingertips. When you look, they are red with blood. Bending down, you gaze at your reflection again in the oven door. Your lip is bust open. Blood trickles down your chin. The oven, still hot, warms your cheeks. You feel safer down here. Out of the way. You take the tea towel from the oven door handle and hold it to your lip. As you stand, tears begin to roll down your face. But you don't say a word. You don't make a sound.

'Oh, here come the waterworks,' he mocks. 'If you didn't touch things that weren't yours, we wouldn't have this problem.'

Maybe he's right, you think, maybe you're the problem. You have nothing to say to him. You wipe your face clean with the tea towel and place it down. There's a tangy taste of metal on your tongue and it makes you wretch.

'You're so dramatic,' he continues. 'It's all for show. It's a little blood, get over yourself.'

You turn towards the drawer to get the carving knife to slice the chicken and to stop him from seeing your eyes twitch with rage. You think about your dad, and what he told you. You know you've let him down.

You turn back around with the knife in hand.

'What the fuck are you planning to do with that, you silly bitch?' he laughs. 'I know you aren't going to try and stab me.'

'The chicken is ready to be carved,' you say softly. You feel the anger rising in the pit of your stomach. Stay calm, you think. You don't want it to get worse.

'Good, because I'm fucking starving. So, hurry your arse up! And stop fucking crying! Your makeup is all over your face. You look like a fucking clown!'

'You *know* what my dad would have to say about *you*?' you snap.

'Your dad ... HA! What would he have to say? Absolutely fuck all, I think.'

You look down so he can't see your face. You grind your teeth together. You don't allow him the satisfaction.

He continues. He is snorting from laughing too hard.

'You make me laugh. Your dad wouldn't say anything. The cancer took him down quick enough,' he chuckles. 'He didn't even fight long enough to get to chemo, silly bitch!'

You look at him and then down at the knife in your hand. And just like that, as quick as flicking a switch, you lunge forwards.

You aren't fast enough. He dodges you, moving out of the way of your stretched arm as you lose your balance and trip into him. He shoves you backwards and you fall, banging your head against the cupboard under the sink. You drop the knife, and it spirals across the floor tiles. Your ribs hurt as you lay there gasping for air.

'ARE YOU KIDDING ME? YOU PSYCHO! DID YOU JUST TRY TO STAB ME?'

You pant as you try to catch your breath.

'You want to try and kill me, huh?' he seethes. 'You want to threaten me?'

Snatching the empty wine bottle by the neck, he smashes it against the kitchen side. The glass shatters and scatters across the room. You cover your face from the shards with the arm that isn't propping you up. He holds the bottleneck with its now jagged end. He stomps towards you, kneels at your eye level, and holds it to your face.

'Try anything like that again, and I'll ram this down your throat and watch you choke to death on your own blood. Simple,' he says.

He waves the sharp glass in front of your eyes. 'Do you understand?'

You're sobbing. All you can do to reply is tremble. You just want it over. You need it to end.

He stands up. Then, he drags you to your feet and gently places the remains of the bottle into your hand.

'Be a doll and clean this up before dinner,' he says smiling.

Clasping the bottleneck tightly, your knuckles turn white. You don't reply.

'Also, you *really* need to go sort your makeup out if you want me to look at you.' He turns and walks towards the door.

You inhale deeply. Mustering all the strength you have left, you charge forwards towards him. You raise your arm, aiming the shards of glass at the side of his neck.

You made sure you were fast enough this time.

Delivery

——Ashleigh Marie Symms——

'WHAT'S THAT?'

    'Oh, it arrived this morning. I thought it was for you.'

    'But it's got your name on it.'

    'Does it? I haven't ordered anything, though. Are you sure—'

    'Just open it.'

    'Is this a joke? I mean—it's from you, isn't it? An early birthday present or—'

    'No, don't be daft. Your birthday isn't for two months.'

    'It's quite heavy. Feel the weight of it—'

    'Open it!'

    'This is from you, don't lie! Is this meant to be funny?'

    'What is it?'

    'You obviously know what it is.'

    'I really don't. What is it?'

    'A Lovehoney Classic Extra Powerful Massage Wand Vibrator.'

    'Ha, no way. Is it really?'

    'This is an expensive joke. I thought you were skint. How much did it set you back?'

    'You really aren't getting any action at the minute, are you?'

    'I DIDN'T BUY IT!'

    'Then who did?'

    'Fuck.'

    'What?'

    'The payment was charged to my bank. Look.'

'So, you did buy it? Why didn't you just open it upstairs—'

'No. It was Eddie.'

'Eddie? I thought you finished with him months ago?'

'I did.'

'What do you mean it was Eddie then?'

'He's been doing weird stuff like this. It hasn't happened for a few weeks … I thought it had stopped.'

'Weird stuff, like what?'

'Using my card to pay for things, sending emails from a fake account pretending to be his brother.'

'How is he using your card?'

'He's memorised the details.'

'You really shouldn't trust anyone with your bank details.'

'I know that *now!* But hindsight's a bitch.'

'Are you sure it's Eddie? He seemed like a nice guy all the times I'd met him.'

'*Seemed* … exactly!'

'Well, what sort of things has he been buying?'

'Weird things … er, a £200 gold chain, a leather jacket, some t-shirts, and other clothes.'

'Are you sure that's all him? I mean … could somebody else have hacked your bank account as well?'

'No, it's all him! He's signed up for one of those catalogues in my name, with my card.'

'Wait … how do you know that?'

'All the things he bought were from the same place.'

'I'm confused.'

'Sorry! Okay, well … I noticed all these payments coming out of my bank, so I contacted the catalogue. They were able to confirm there was an account under my name, but when they looked into the orders, they managed to trace it back to Eddie's email and address.'

'Right. So—hold on—have you called the police?'

'Yeah.'

'They haven't done anything?'

'There is a warrant out for his arrest.'

'And?'

'He's never in when they go to his house.'

'Is there nothing else they can do?'

'They basically just told me to hang tight.'

'What the fuck! He's harassing you!'

'That's what the warrant is for. Harassment and fraud.'

'He could be stalking you. Stalking *us* and watching the flat for all we know.'

'Don't say that.'

'How are you so calm about this?'

'The police are handling it. That reminds me, I'm going to need to call and report this vibrator—'

'I'm sure that won't be awkward ... but they're hardly handling it if he keeps doing it. How can you feel safe?'

'I'm trying not to think about it too much. That's what Eddie wants ... to scare us.'

'Well, it's working. It's scaring me! What did the emails say?'

'The emails?'

'From his brother's account?'

'Oh, yeah! They were odd ... warning me to stay away from Eddie because he's a dangerous guy ... Stuff like that.'

'Could the emails not be from his brother?'

'He doesn't have a brother!'

'Okay ... yeah, that's weird! I'm officially freaked out now. Aren't you scared?'

'A little.'

'Why didn't you say anything before?'

'Didn't want you to worry.'

'You should have told me!'

'I'm sorry.'

'It's okay, but tell me next time ... so, how do we know the vibrator is from him?'

'Well, to be honest … I suppose we don't. But it's pretty obvious!'

'But it hasn't come from a catalogue. It's from Lovehoney. Look at the box.'

'He sent me a package from there a few weeks ago. It was this leather-look bra with cut-outs where your nipples would be. There was a note inside too. It said, "This would look great on you!" I recognised his handwriting … I know this is him again.'

'Why didn't I see this?'

'You were at Adam's for the weekend. I called the police, and they came round and took it for evidence.'

'What's he getting out of all of this?'

'Nothing, he just likes mind games. He sent some rock to my mum last week.'

'Rocks? Do you mean like gravel or bricks—'

'No, no! Rock that you eat … a stick of seaside rock, like from Blackpool.'

'Well, how is that malicious?'

'It's a play, a move in his game. It's his way of saying I still remember where your mum lives.'

'But why?'

'I don't know.'

'No—I mean—why rock?'

'Oh! We went to Wales one weekend, and we brought some back for my mum. He must've remembered she liked it.'

'It's like the start of a horror film.'

'Don't be so dramatic!'

'I can't believe I thought he was a nice guy.'

'Neither can I.'

'And you slept with him! Uh … that's made my skin crawl.'

'I should've picked up on the red flags from that. He was into all that kinky stuff in the bedroom. He always wanted to be in control in there too.'

'That'll explain the bra and vibrator then … I honestly can't get my head around this. I don't believe it.'

'It'll all be okay. The police will arrest him eventually.'

'Until then?'

'We stay calm … and by "we", I mean you.'

'Yeah, you're probably right. I'm just overreacting.'

'Yes, yes you are. If anyone should be freaking out, it should be me!'

'Yeah, he's just a weirdo. What a dick … but we will double-check the door is locked before bed?'

'Yes.'

'And we'll do a background check on all your future boyfriends?'

'Ha, ha! Very funny!'

'You know, on the bright side, there is one good thing to come out of this...'

'What's that?'

'The vibrator comes with batteries.'

A Venture to Journey's End

——*Emily Crawford*——

THE WAY WAS SHUT.

Carrion birds cried. Their ragged black shadows flying overhead, taking the easy path.

Everything that lay before him was high in the sky. Islands were perched atop vines that hung from the faces of cliffs and reached far into the mists below. Rocks rolled and tumbled off the edges, clattering and smashing into one another as they remained suspended in the air. Water rushed, pouring out from every crack and disappearing down into the void. Its spray was like rain, with droplets of dew clinging to the overgrowth that twisted from the gardens above.

Everything that came before was gone, consumed by mist. The way was shut; he had to make the climb.

⁂

'Oh! I'm sorry, I didn't mean to.'

'No really, it was my fault. I'm sorry, I really didn't mean to.'

'My- my name? Oh, my name is Faye. What's yours?'

'Griffin? Huh?'

'You're named after a monster?'

⁂

The ground was swallowed by thick fog. It was as if he had climbed into a storm. Caught in the wind, the cloud shifted and formed towering plumes to obscure the path. There was already rain. The water which ran over the stone and pattered on the overgrowth had soaked through his leathers. But now there was thunder. A low

32

rumble, a cheap imitation, as the displaced rocks battered together and shook the islands above.

He was climbing to the heights of the hanging isles, navigating between the jagged cliffs and the wrapping vines which connected them all.

The shards and thorns pierced through his gloves, tore at his leathers. He could feel the blood, wet and warm, starting to stick to his palms. It peeled and broke every time he reached upward; he felt the congealed threads snap.

❧

'Griffin? What's wrong?'

'Are you sure?'

'Look, if you want, I can leave? I- I don't mind.'

'Okay, okay! I'll stay … But please just tell me?'

'What are you talking about? Yes! Yes! Of course I will!'

❧

He could no longer hear the droplets of water mimic the rain. He could hear the world above. The gurgling of the rivers' currents and the rushing of the waterfalls at their end. The cries of the carrion birds perched on the tree's branches and the rustling of the wildlife in the gardens.

He continued his climb.

The vines had become roots, erupting from the stone and earth to support the surrounding isles. Laid out like a web above him, they interconnected each island, each path, each way through the fog. They were covered in amber crystals, hardened sap that glimmered and reflected the worlds below. Each one was alive. The images rippling like waves as he climbed past them. These were the sights of the Yggdrasil, and its gardens were not much further.

❧

'No evil shall befall you, on hill nor bank …'

'In field or valley, on mountain or glen …'

'Neither above nor below …'

'Neither in sea, nor–'

'Griffin? Who are they?'

33

※

The excretion was jellied but smooth. It was an oil which coated the rough bark and over time hardened to create new countries, new worlds. It would have been mesmerising if it was not so dangerous.

At the heights, his footing was wavering, and his grip was uncertain. He reached up and failed to dig his fingers into the fractures. There was a click, a snap. Then nothing. His hand was numb. He was falling. His legs were flailing. Loose stone scattered into the air as he slid. He stopped breathing, biting through his lip and feeling the blood pool at the back of his throat. Pulling himself up, the bone in his wrist crumbled. He bit harder, catching himself with his other hand before he dropped.

He was dangling above the void, the wind blowing between his legs and catching the ends of his cloak. He strained and struggled, his body burning as he hoisted himself up. Kicking his legs against the broken stone, he scurried up and onto the length of the root.

※

'You lied to me, Griffin. You said that was the end of it.'

'No, it's not. You promised me!'

'You told me all of that was behind you!'

'Okay … Okay, I trust you …'

'I love you too.'

※

Bent on all fours, he coughed up the blood he had refused to swallow. It ran through the crevices and dripped down and into the void. Dashes of the mist turned red, becoming crimson wisps caught in the wind. He clutched the bark. He was trembling. But he cast his eyes upwards.

Burning away the fog, a white light shone through the canopy of Yggdrasil. It shone upon its leaves and ignited its fruit like the fires of a roaring hearth. The tips of the standing stones towered high and atop them, the yellow eyes of the ragged black shadows watched him. The mess of roots hung over the edge of the island, but the path lay before him. Cobbles twisted and trapped within its growth. It was the path few had ever trod, but it would lead him to journey's end.

He snapped a few small twigs from the root beneath him and stuck them into his glove. For now, they would need to be enough to support the break in his hand. Shakily he rose to his feet, trying to find his balance as he lifted himself onto the path and over the final hurdle.

🐚

'Why are they here?'

'Griffin, what do they want?'

'Griffin? What are you doing?'

'You're sorry? Griffin, you're scaring me.'

'Stop! Get away! Get away!'

🐚

Keeping his shattered hand pressed against his chest, he made his way along the path. He passed under the shadows of the standing stones, seeing the runes for life, death, and everything in between crudely carved into the rock.

The click of his heel echoed and frightened the carrion birds, sending the flock flying into the refuge of the treetops. But the beasts of this place were not startled. They watched him with intrigue. Strange, white-furred beasts, prey and predator alike, all shimmering with a haunting blue glow. Their empty eyes pierced him. They turned him hollow.

He tried to ignore them, taking a knee before the ruined altar which lay beneath the mighty yew. The stones had collapsed, toppled by the roots of the tree. The runes and wards had been rubbed away, fading under a growth of mildew and moss. Puddles of hardened wax marked where the prayer candles once stood. It was true. This place had been abandoned by all worlds.

He dusted the surface and set his own candles in a circle. He lit each one, carefully cupping the flame to protect it from the wind and encourage it to catch the wick. Then he searched his pack, taking from it her ring and a lock of her hair and placing it in the centre of the altar. Every movement he made was awkward, compensating for his injury.

Here, at the journey's end where all worlds became one, he would bring her back. He closed his eyes and said the prayer.

The wards singed the moss, glowing a brilliant blue as the winds entrapped him. The carrion birds crowed, and the animals fled. Yggdrasil shook. Its leaves falling to the ground below. He opened his eyes and spoke her name.

The candles were extinguished.

The way was shut.

Good Girl

——Genoviev Aviles——

I NEVER KNEW LOVE UNTIL yesterday. The warmth I felt is unexplainable, but I'll try my best.

A simple white home. A white fence surrounds lush green grass. The mustache man with the kind eyes and white lab coat smiled down at me. He carried me like a newborn.

'Be nice, Laika,' he whispered to me.

I looked down at two small children. The young girl had her hair up with some sort of puffy thing. The man put me down. I looked up at him. He nodded in the direction of the children. I don't know what to do. It's the first time in two years I've been outside of that cage. Was this a trick?

My memory is fuzzy. I don't remember much of my time outside the cage. All I remembered was being cold, wet, and hungry.

The grass felt wet and soft between my paws. I pressed into the dirt. I looked at the mud hugging the sides of my claws. It's mushy and watery. It felt amazing. It smells of freedom. I looked up at the man. He smiled. The girl reached and took me into her arms.

'Careful, Anya,' the man said.

She kissed me on my forehead. 'What a good girl.'

I've only dreamt of being told that. I never thought someone would say it to me. I'm just a mutt from the middle of nowhere.

I licked her face. What a strange taste, difficult to process the flavor. Salty? Maybe tangy? Her eyes are large and green. Her laugh made my heart flutter. My tail wagged at the sound of her high pitch laugh. I don't think I've ever made someone giggle.

'Does she bite, Dad?' asked the little boy.

'No, Lev,' the mustachioed man says.

The little boy reached and scratched the back of my ear. I felt goosebumps all through my tiny body. What an extraordinary feeling. I nuzzled at his hand; he continued to scratch me. His warmth felt so lovely. Lev and Anya. Are they my first home? I think I'd like that.

'She looks like a boy,' Lev said.

Anya lightly pets my lashes, 'Are you kidding? Look at those lashes.'

The boy squinted and shook his head.

Boy? Girl? What did they mean? I'm me. It doesn't matter, as long as I stayed with my new family.

The man with the mustache handed them something. 'See if she'll chase it.'

Lev threw the thing straight towards me. It's some bouncy circle. I ran away, cowered, and wagged my tail between my legs. How dare they throw something so scary!

'You're supposed to chase it,' he grabbed the ball, threw it, and ran after it. 'See.'

I didn't understand what he was trying to do. My ears perked as I tilted my head in confusion.

'You're throwing it too hard,' Anya said.

She grabbed the ball and held it down to me. I sniffed and licked it.

Anya giggled, 'It's not food. It's to play with.'

She lightly bounced the ball; my eyes followed every bounce. Up, down, up, and down again. My tail wagged as I tried to reach for it and flip over. Anya and Lev laughed. Anya threw the ball, and I ran after it. The wind felt weird inside of my ears. I didn't care. I chased after the bouncy thing.

I could hear the sounds of what Lev calls crickets as I grabbed the ball a final time. I chewed on the ball as I trotted my way back to Anya and Lev.

Anya patted her leg. 'Bring it here.'

'No, here,' Lev said.

I looked at both. Who do I give the ball to? They are the sweetest children I could imagine as my own. I'm one lucky dog.

'Dinner is ready,' their dad called from inside of a house. My mouth watered as I looked at my plate. It's some meat covered in sauce.

Lev picks up his fork. 'Are you sure she can eat this?'

His dad shoved a spoonful of beef stroganoff into his mouth. 'Of course.'

I didn't wait for anyone's approval and dug in. I couldn't help myself. I half-swallowed/chewed my food. My mouth was covered in a thick creamy sauce. My tongue tingled from the flavors.

Anya looks down at me. 'It's good, huh?'

Good? I thought the bouncy ball was terrific. This surpassed it, and it was all mine. I licked the bowl clean. This was the best day of my life.

After dinner, Anya and Lev took me to their room. Two small brown beds, blocks, and dolls cover the floor. An assortment of clothes was piled high in a corner. Their room smelled like tobacco, like the rest of the house.

Anya grabbed a pillow and put a thick blanket over it. 'This is your bed.'

Something that belonged to me. I jumped and rolled around my new bed. It felt like a thousand of those bouncy balls, soft.

'I think she likes her bed,' Lev laughed.

This was the kindest gesture anyone had ever done for me. They gave me my place in their home. I had never felt more at home than I did then. I went in circles, trying to find the perfect spot.

'Do you think this is the first time she's ever had a bed?' Anya asked.

That's weird. They should've known this. Hasn't their dad said anything?

Lev shrugged.

'Time for bed, Laika has a big day tomorrow,' their dad said from outside of their room.

Anya's eyes went wide. 'Why?'

Her dad looked around the room. 'It's just a busy day.'

'Can we take her to the park tomorrow?' Lev asked.

'Only if you finish your homework,' their dad said.

'Poppa, she's staying with us, right?' Anya asked as she petted me.

'Of course,' he looked away. 'Don't forget to give her a bath before—' He looked down at the paw prints I left on the blanket.

Lev picks me up. 'We will.'

The children got ready for bed. They did this weird thing called brushing their teeth. It looked painful if you asked me.

Lev grabbed a towel. 'Laika, come here.'

I hid behind the door. I wasn't dumb enough to go in there. I knew a bath when I saw one.

'You have to be clean, or Poppa will make you sleep outside,' Anya picks me up. 'C'mon.'

I struggled, but she managed to put me in a tub full of bubbles.

'I promise, if you behave, I will give you more stroganoff for breakfast.'

I perked my ears. Seconds? I no longer struggled. The water was warm, unlike back in the cage. It soothed my sore muscles from running.

Lev wrapped me up in a thick towel and carried me like a baby. 'See, you're such a good girl.'

He put me in front of a mirror, and I couldn't recognize the canine in front of me. The white of my fur contrasted with my brown and black spots. My dirt-stained belly was no more.

Lev kissed my forehead. 'Time for bed.'

A beautiful field was full of balls and stroganoff. Lev and Anya were there running around and laughing with me.

'I love you, Laika,' they both said.

I ran towards them kissed their faces and arms.

Rough hands woke me up. 'Be quiet.'

I tried to bite the hand over my mouth.

I felt a sharp needle pain on my backside. 'Stop it. You'll wake them up.'

The hand covered my mouth as I went in and out of consciousness.

It's dark. I was in a small room. No windows, nothing. SPUTNIK 2 was written on a wall. Where are Lev and Anya? Where Am I? What's going on? It was warm, too warm.

'Laika,' a voice said.

I looked around but there was no one. I couldn't tell where it was coming from. My heart raced and I struggled to breathe. I ran in circles looking for the owner of the voice. I barked at nothing. I'm all alone.

'Laika, calm down, everything is okay.'

I couldn't concentrate. Where is my family? My forever home? I felt a tightness in my chest. My heart shattered. I trembled in the darkness. I peed.

'She's losing oxygen. The central R-7sustainer has failed. She's overheating as well,' a woman stated.

Huh? What does that mean?

'Sir, she won't survive much longer in orbit,' she stated.

'Is there anything we can do?' a man asked.

'You told us not to make a recovery or survival plan, sir.'

Silence.

Every breath felt short. My chest hurt. I just wanted to go home. Why was I here? Why was I wearing this weird contraption? I opened my mouth wider, but it was no use. It hurt to breathe. I wanted to be in my kids' arms.

'Laika, it's me,' another voice said.

I knew that voice. It was Anya and Lev's dad!

He's going to save me. I howl. It hurts my chest.

'Everything is going to be okay,' he whispers.

Every breath feels like a distant memory I struggle to remember.

'Lev and Anya love you so much. I don't think they will ever forgive me. I just wanted you to know what it felt like to have a home before...'

All I heard was that they loved me. They loved me for me. Just a mutt from the streets. Then why was I here? I could feel thick bubbles blur my vision.

'Just know if they had given me a choice. I would have kept you.'

'Just remember, this was for science,' the woman interrupted.

I fell over. I didn't have the strength to stand up. I felt light-headed and struggled to keep my eyes open. Anya. Lev.

'You are such a good girl,' he said.

Maybe I wasn't good enough.

Three Stages of Twilight

—— *Chris Appleyard* ——

SUSAN PLACED HER COFFEE MUG beside the pile of travel brochures on her balcony table and looked out over the roaring M90, past the aluminium plated Armadillo, to the hills on the south side of Glasgow. The Alexander 'Greek' Thompson church spires and the merchants' towers overlooking the Clyde were so sharply defined in the clear air, she felt as if she could reach out and touch them.

During the sixties and seventies, the smog had turned day into night; the Ravenscraig steelworks spewed out sparking flames, turning the sky a diabolical red. Even in daylight it could be difficult to see what was in front of your nose.

There were no descriptions of gaseous steelworks or of the crescendoing animalistic roars from football stadiums in the Enid Blyton books she'd read when she was wee. She'd dreamt of being one of the Famous Five, sharing their adventures, their confidence that whatever challenges they faced, they would come up trumps. Most of all, she wanted to share their picnics. Cream teas and ginger pop hadn't featured in her family's Sunday outings to the murky pond in Queen's Park where even the swans seemed depressed; she got a dribbling ice cream oyster from the creepy man in the tinkly van and a bottle of cream soda, if she was lucky.

Shielding her eyes, she made out the faint buttery-yellow haze of gorse on the Cathkin Braes.

She remembered a sepia photograph in her gran's album; ladies in white linen dresses, parasols protecting their fine Scottish skin, their backs corset-straight as they sat on tartan travelling rugs, applauding moustachioed men in white flannels.

Now the Castlemilk housing estate, or 'Chateau du lait', as the Glasgow taxi drivers called the vast scheme, surrounded the Braes. The tennis courts had been torn up to make way for bouncy trampolines the size of small unstable planets. Maybe the planners hadn't meant for it to be as bad as it had turned out. Hindsight was a fine thing. But the men who'd profited from the regeneration weren't the displaced Gorbals' folk, stuck in their harled hell.

The library in the council estate precinct had been the only one left open in her neighbourhood at the height of the three-day week. Even then, stray dogs roamed the streets feeding on discarded fish suppers from mountains of fly-blown rubbish left uncollected on the pavement.

Once, she'd walked home, art books under her arm, when a gawky lad with a greyhound that was missing a front leg stopped her on the path across the field to her house. He'd asked her the time. And then he'd exposed himself. Most likely he'd been sniffing glue at the back of the Cathkin Hotel. When she thought about that day, it wasn't his penis clutched in his sticky fist she remembered, it was the greyhound. Memory was a slippery thing.

Moving from the balcony into the small sitting room, she collapsed the clotheshorse and gazed at the picture hanging above the flame-effect gas fire. She'd just left Art School and, throwing caution and six months' rent to the wind, had bid for the painting in an auction just off Garnethill Road. It'd survived her flat shares and the subsequent house moves as she ascended the snakes and ladders of the property market.

Ali had said it was too big for her new flat, it needed a larger 'space', an airy room, to really show it off to its best advantage. He wasn't backward in coming forward with his opinions, just like his dear departed father. She looked again at the painting squashed between the mock pine mantelpiece and the artexed ceiling. He was right, though. To really appreciate the painting, to get the right perspective, you couldn't be too close, you needed to step back. Who were these people; the man with the horse and cart, the wee lad at the close door, and the woman staring out of the window, her washing hanging on the drooping grey line? How could she have got her sheets so white? Artistic license perhaps. Susan smiled. She knew all about that.

If she decided to let the painting go, it'd be the woman she'd miss the most. There was a dignity about her, a strength. It felt as if the artist had known these folk intimately. George Walker had been over-looked in his own lifetime, but now his paintings were collected by those who wouldn't know a Gorbals' single end from the back end of a Glasgow bus.

She glanced at her watch. Better get herself ready.

The floor to ceiling bedroom mirrors caught her unaware. Multiple versions of herself crowded towards her from every angle, cornering her, hemming her in. She took a deep breath and stared at her reflection. Who in the name of God wanted to see themselves in such uncompromising detail? It was bad enough with your clothes on, but naked, in the full light of day. She drew the blinds; darkness hid a multitude of sin.

Her mobile phone pinged as she walked back into the sitting room.

BE OUTSIDE IN 5. WON'T COME UP KIDS MIGHT STEAL STUFF.

Indeed, they might.

The lift smelt of urine and sweet cigarette smoke but at least it was working. She pressed the button. GROUND FLOOR LOBBY. Ground floor lobby. What did they think they'd built, the bloody Ritz?

In the concrete play area surrounding the flats, children wheeled about on thick-tyred bikes like scavenging gulls. She'd bought the twins bikes when they were wee. Not top of the range or anything. No 'Thank You' letter, of course. Her mother had been keen on good manners, keeping up appearances, even though they lived in a prefab and her dad had enjoyed a light refreshment or two, as they used to say. What would they say now; he'd ongoing issues with the imbibement of alcohol-related substances, or something. Really, he was just an alky: a disappointed man, big on swagger, small in stature, the same as so many Glaswegian men.

Children played different games now, on the computer. In her day, they'd stoated hard rubber balls against harled garage walls,

First leggy second leggy
jibby and through,
back bridgey burly

and I love you.

and played skipping games in the street,

Murder murder three stairs up

the mannie in the middle door

hut me wae a cup

ma heeds aw broken ma face aw cut

murder murder polis three stairs up.

A white Range Rover drew up in front of her. Susan waved through the tinted glass and tugged at the door handle.

The window lowered. 'It's electric, Mother, don't yank it like that.'

She'd travelled this route a thousand times, sitting on the top of the number 20 bus clutching a sodden satchel, her damp blazer smelling like her family's old Labrador, gazing at the blackened buildings, the vestiges of an Empire she'd learned about from the oil-cloth maps in cold classrooms: the familiar landmarks of her once flourishing city.

The Land Rover, a sealed unit of silence, navigated the old Glasgow Cross with its clock faces and the city's coat of arms. What was the wee poem?

The bell that never rang

the fish that didn't swim, was that right?

The bird that never flew.

And something about a tree.

She turned towards her son. 'What does the tree represent, Ali? In the Glasgow poem?'

'Poem? What are you talking about? What poem?'

The Arts were never his thing. Not even nursery rhymes. When he was wee, he'd thrown the Golden Book of Children's Verse out of the window, screaming he wanted an Action Man annual. His father had been delighted when she'd told him about that.

'It doesn't matter, Ali. I was just thinking about the wee poem on the coat of arms, that's all. But it doesn't matter.'

Wiping a blur of condensation off the passenger seat window with her buttoned sleeve, she peered out. There was probably air-con in the car, but she didn't like to ask.

The Rhul Bingo Hall across the street had been a cinema in her day. Technicolour Western posters displayed a grizzled John Wayne and his handsome sidekick, herding long-horn cattle across the Rio Grande, heading to dusty towns and bawdy bars. When it had been covered by a Goldfinger poster, she'd felt as if a part of her soul had been pasted over.

'Here we are then.' His voice, so like his father's, pulled her from the fantasy of the Texas sun, back to the grey stone of south-side suburbia.

Alistair jumped from the leather driving seat, strode up the steps and opened the stained-glass front door; etched fruit spilled from a cornucopia of plenty.

Susan followed.

Monday, Tuesday, Wednesday, Thursday, Friday, Saturday, Sunday.

Childhood games. Childish shrieks. The terror of capture and surrender.

Susan slipped off her coat and folded it over her arm. Placing her palm on the cool wall, she gazed up the stairwell toward the roof light. 'Oh, you've had the hallway painted.'

'Yes. Farrow and Ball, "Polar Bear's Pelt". It cost a fortune. We like the chalkiness of the white.'

She remembered her husband's drawn face as he stood in the same hallway, yelling directions at the men from Pickford's.

'Polar Bear's Belt, Ali, well … that is … different.'

Yesterday upon the stairs I met a man who wasn't there,

he wasn't there again today,

I wish that man would go away.

How could she make light of it? Hugh's temper was never, ever, a joke. She remembered the feel of the worn leather belt as she tried to yank it out of his clenched hand when he removed it from the thin loops on his ill-fitting trousers. He believed in discipline. Thought that his son should be disciplined, in the same way as he had been, in his boarding school, up in that unforgiving Scottish Glen.

Strange how the mind reframed events to make them more bearable.

46

'What? What?'

'The Polar Bear, Ali. The Polar Bear's belt.'

'For God's sake Mother, *pelt*. Polar Bear's *pelt*.'

'Oh, yes. I see. Well, that is clever isn't it. Do you think they skinned the Polar Bear and sold the pelt?'

'What? Who? For Heaven's sake what are you talking about now? It's just the name of the bloody paint!'

'Ah, yes, the name of the bloody paint.'

The new kitchen looked out into the garden, sliding glass doors led onto wooden decking.

'It all looks lovely, Ali.' Susan turned, hanging her coat over the high spindle-backed chair. 'You and Penny must be delighted with everything you've acquired.'

'Yes, we are. Hard work of course. But I'm not afraid of hard work, and neither is Penny. Although she is working part-time now. Dad instilled the need for hard work in me from an early age, hard work and discipline. As you know.'

'Yes.' Susan gazed out, through the fragile glass boundary, onto the unfamiliar garden. 'Your father always did have a strong sense of both.'

They'd met at a city secondary school when he'd interviewed her for a temporary teaching post.

> *Oor wee school's the best wee school, the best wee school in glesga*
> *the only thing that's wrang wi it is the baldy heeded maister*
> *he goes tae the pub oan a saturday nicht 'n goes tae church on sunday tae pray tae god*
> *tae gie hum strength tae belt awe the weans oan monday.*

Art wasn't a priority at the school, as he'd explained, but he needed a qualified teacher to tick the right boxes. God, she'd been naïve. Straight from Art School, straight from a failed relationship with the ubiquitous, lascivious art lecturer —Brutalist Art in the Urban Environment—to an inner-city school, and the bed of a thrusting young headmaster.

Matrimony, child, miscarriage. A failed relationship, uncoupled by an unexpected embolism.

One potato two potato three potato four,

five potato six potato seven potato more,

you are out with a dirty rottin clout

right ower your face…

just like this!

'And where's Penny? And the twins? I haven't seen them for ages. I thought they'd be here. Aren't they coming?'

'Of course.' He moved towards the reclaimed Belfast sink, filled the kettle. 'Just off to pick up a few things from Waitrose. We're having friends round for dinner tonight. I'm making a coffee. Do you want one?'

She stared at the back of his head, felt the familiar tingle of unexpressed rage prick her scalp. 'If it's not too much trouble.'

'D'you want a biscuit?' He rummaged in the tin, 'Only got digestives left. Happy Birthday by the way.'

A digestive biscuit. A bloody digestive biscuit. After all she'd done. Staying with his father, keeping up appearances, handing over the house to accommodate his growing family, moving to that tiny flat, for a bloody McVitie's digestive biscuit and a mug of instant coffee. She thought, for once, they would have managed a shop bought cake and a bottle of red.

Does yer ma drink wine

does she drink it all the time

does she get a funny feelin' when her belly hits the ceiling…?

But no, a stale biscuit and coffee as weak as dirty bathwater. Well, at least now she knew exactly where she stood. She'd more than done her bit, if she sold the painting there'd be absolutely no guilt.

Sipping her coffee, she smoothed the creases from her dress. 'Thank you, Ali. Yes, a digestive would be … fine.'

'So,' his knee bounced, sploshing coffee over the table. 'So, how're things at the flat?'

Susan nibbled the edge of her biscuit. 'Fine, everything's fine at the flat. Settling in. Some of the neighbours are … interesting.'

'Good. Yes, that's good.' He brushed an imaginary crumb from his knee onto the slate floor. 'And your things? Enough room for all your things?'

Enough room for all her things? What things? The things she'd taken to the coup when he'd encouraged her to downsize.

'Well, thanks for asking, Ali. Very thoughtful. It's absolutely fine, what with the fitted wardrobes and the magnolia.' She sipped her bitter coffee.

'And how about the picture? Are you finding it a tad depressing, what with all that working-class squalor? Penny was just saying that some nice Japanese prints would suit the space better. More minimal.'

She gazed at her son. Nice Japanese prints. More minimal. Christ, he had literally no idea. Just like his bloody father. 'I'm no great fan of Japonica thank you, Alistair, whatever its dimensions.'

'Yes, well, I suppose going to Art School does leave some sort of mark on you.' His mobile's ringtone pierced the suburban silence. He grabbed it from his chinos' pocket, strode across the floor, stabbed the green button, and tugged open the folding glass doors. Warm air carried with it the sound of lawnmowers, the scent of cut grass and melting tar.

'What? No. Not yet. Christ, keep your voice down. OK I was just about to actually. Yes, later. See you later.'

'That sounded like Penny. Is she on her way? Nothing wrong, I hope.' She glanced at her son. 'You're looking awfully red Ali, is it the heat?'

'Wrong? No, not at all. Nothing's wrong. Do you want to go into the sitting room? It's cooler in there, north facing.'

North facing? What was he on about? Surely not the damned Polar Bears again. 'No, I'm fine Ali. Very comfortable. Quite at home in fact.'

'So … I wanted to talk to you about … It's roasting in here. Hot as hell.' She waited.

'The twins are both starting at Craighall next month. We're delighted, of course, that they've got in_…'

'Your Dad used to say that all you needed to get into that school was a father who could write a cheque. He could be quite amusing sometimes, your father.'

'Could he? Yes … well, he could be many things, as you know.' He slumped down opposite her. She felt the penetration of his gaze. How much did he remember? Not much surely, he was only a child after all. And he'd adored his father, hadn't he.

'Anyway, the thing is, the fees are quite expensive. Not undoable of course. But expensive.' He raked his hands through his hair. Receding just like his father's. Soon he'd be as bald as a coot.

'I see, Ali.' Susan traced a tight circle with her finger on the warm wooden table. 'Well, I'm very glad the fees are doable. That must be a relief to you both.'

He looked like that swan in the pond when children threw chunks of Mother's Pride at its bent head. Unruffled on the outside but paddling furiously below the murky surface.

'Yes, it is a relief. It's a relief that we can just about afford to send our children to a school where they can be themselves, feel safe.'

Sunlight caught the mock Rennie Macintosh clock on the wall. She glanced over his balding head.

'Good. That's good, feeling safe is important. Anyway, I need to go to the bathroom before I leave you. If you'll excuse me?'

The old Armitage Shanks had been ripped out, the original cast iron bath replaced by a walk-in shower and matching vanity units.

Susan sat on the oak toilet seat. The suddenness of Hugh's stroke. Watching him as he struggled to get out of the bath. He would've hated to die like that. Undignified. Vulnerable. His penis, like a sea slug, wafting in the cold scummy water.

I had a little monkey his name was Tiny Tim
I put him in the bath to see if he could swim
he drank all the water
he ate all the soap
and he died last night with a bubble in his throat.
With a bubble in his throat.
He died last night, with a bubble in his throat.
Down the stairs, into the kitchen, a quick 'cheerio'.
Exit stage left. Followed by bears. Out of the etched door and into the garden.
Sunday Saturday Friday Thursday Wednesday Tuesday Monday.

The bus crossed the Clyde on the George V bridge. The Waverley steamer chugged tourists out towards the mouth of the river, past the M90, and the Merchant City.

The Armadillo, claws retracted, crouched on its silted bank. Susan took in the view of the city from the top deck. It wasn't the view she'd dreamt of, but perhaps, if she sold the painting, she'd have options. Just a matter of testing the water. She sat back, luxuriating in the familiar heat of the leatherette seat, thinking about her hidden poster, about crossing the Rio Grande, under the blazing Texan sun.

The Man in the Boot

—— *Callum McGee* ——

LAURIE WAS ALREADY STANDING AT the curb when I pulled up outside her flat. Two large duffle bags lay at her feet. The black Ford parked in front sagged into the road, its tyres slashed.

I jumped out to grab her bags. She wrapped her arms around my neck and kissed me on the mouth. Her breath was cool and cloudy.

'What took you so long, Albie?' Laurie said.

'Work trouble.' I escorted her to the passenger seat, bowing as I opened the door. She giggled and snuggled into her fur coat. I carried the bags round the back of my Merc and set them down. I waited a moment, straining to hear any sound from inside the boot. All was quiet. I popped it open, one hand gripping the knife under my shirt, but the body lying there hardly stirred. I felt something wet land on my shoe and looked down. Piss. That's what I got for smashing the bald prick's specs. I pulled off his tie and pressed it against the stains. Not much could be done for the smell. I nudged him to make room for the bags, then shut the boot.

'Good thing you get the bus to work,' I said, getting behind the wheel.

Laurie frowned at the vandalised Ford. 'Take me away now.'

I pulled away, slowly going over potholes. Laurie didn't seem to mind the occasional heavy thump from the boot. It could have been the bags.

It felt good to get onto the dual carriageway. It wasn't ideal having Baldie along with us, but it settled me down knowing with every mile clocked up we were further from the city. A welcome gust of wind blasted through Laurie's open window.

'How's your week been?' I said.

'Shite. I was desperate to get out of there.'

'Me too,' I said and turned on the radio.

'Don't you want to hear about it?'

'What's that?' I lowered the volume.

'Why it was so shite. And why I wish we were leaving that fucking city for the last time.'

'Aye, go on. Might as well get it all out. Don't want you testy when we get there.'

Laurie closed her window. 'Testy? Some cheek.'

'Don't want none of us testy, I mean. Not this weekend.'

'I'm not testy.' The wind had messed up her hair, and she fussed over it using a mirror.

'Okay, you're not. Come on, tell me about it.'

'You sure you want to hear?' Laurie put the mirror back in her handbag.

'Course. Three years. Can tell me anything.'

'Three years.' Laurie smiled and locked her fingers in mine while I kept the other hand on the wheel. I was about to return her smile when she set off on one of her rants.

'Mr Gibson, oh, I've got to tell you about Mr Gibson.'

'It's Gibson's turn again.'

'That fat pig! He kept us all behind last night an extra two hours. And do you know what? No fucking overtime!'

'I think you already told me all this in those texts—'

'Two hours! It's like the pig doesn't know we've got lives outside his shitehole bar.' I waited as Laurie wound herself tighter. She tapped her heel against the floor mat. Her rage seemed to come from the lower half of her body.

'And then, this morning when I was looking for something nice to wear to surprise you, I caught this creep ogling me from across the lingerie aisle. To think people like this are wandering our streets sharing the same oxygen as us.'

'Did he leave you alone?' I glanced at her shaking leg. 'Why don't you take off your boots?'

Laurie unbuckled her seatbelt then bent down to pull her boots off. She spoke between grunts. 'Oh, you better believe it. For a minute I faked not seeing him, then turned and marched towards him wielding a clothes hanger. He quickly fucked off. Should have seen the state of him.' She seemed lighter after taking her big boots off. Without putting her belt back on she set her seat back and lifted her sweaty feet over the glove compartment.

'He can't be as grim as some of the customers you get at the bar though,' I said.

'Maybe not, but there was something really dodgy about him. I can't imagine the lunatics people like that associate with. It makes me want to spew. I'm telling you, I'd have really went for him if he got any closer.' Laurie examined her sharp fingernails like she was thinking about the damage they could do. 'Anyway, how's you?'

'You know, managing. Had a problem at the office today. That's why I was a bit late in picking you up.'

'What happened?'

'Jim didn't turn up for a meeting with a client.'

'Fucking Jim. He always lets you down, Albie.'

'I think the meeting went alright without him though. I pitched the guy my ideas and he seemed impressed.'

Laurie squeezed my arm and rested her head against my shoulder. It wasn't long till she was dozing and whistling through her nose. I listened for other sounds. Just cars ripping along the dual carriageway.

The meeting had not been alright. That lunchtime I'd waited over an hour at the garage, but Roger didn't turn up. He'd been late before, but never as bad as that. Without him to collect I was just an utter roaster with a handcuffed prick in my car. I called Roger but it went straight to voicemail. I always knew one day he'd fuck me over. Something about his face, too rat-like to be trusted. No idea what Kenny saw in him.

Kenny ordered who needed sorting out. He never told me what they'd done, just gave me the basics: what they looked like, where they lived, what time they went to work. I didn't need much more than that. As long as I picked up my envelope at the end of it all, I was happy. I tried Kenny but he didn't answer either.

After a quick Google search, I'd bought a packet of Promethazine from a pharmacy, then driven about the city searching for a quiet spot. All the while the man thrashed about in the boot and my phone kept dinging with message after message from Laurie. She always did this, as if it would speed up time before we met. I got out my other phone from the glove compartment. What about Rachel, the other woman in my life? Still just an 'ok' from her. Being away for the weekend on important business apparently didn't deserve a better response. She didn't even care where I was going.

I eventually found an abandoned office block across from the river. The car park was overgrown with weeds and littered with traffic cones and broken glass. When I opened the boot, the man flopped about like a slippery fish. I waved the packet of tablets at him.

'You're going to take these, Baldie. All of them.'

He stopped moving to see what I was holding. His eyes widened. The flopping started up again with a few groans thrown in. I pulled out my knife and he became still.

'No shouting, okay? This is a shite day for you being in my life.' I grabbed his wee sausage legs and heaved him onto the ground in an upright position. His specs slipped off. I stamped on them and placed them back on his face, cracked and wonky. 'I got you water 'cause I'm a sound guy.' When I tore the duct tape from his mouth his breath was quick and dry against my hand. I paused to take him in, slumped there with his potbelly and pointy laced-up shoes. A shirt button was missing from when I grabbed him earlier. I grinned at the memory. One by one I fed him the tablets, sending a scoosh of water down after them. The colour drained from his face, and his lips trembled. As soon as he gulped down the last tablet I stuck more tape to his mouth, pulled him up by his sweaty pits and pushed him back into the boot.

The river rippled under an overcast sky. A flock of geese swooped down to skim the water but thought better of it and adjusted their course. It'd taken no more than half an hour for the car to become still. The silence had calmed me for a bit till I got another ding from Laurie.

The sky still had that dreich look about it. It didn't matter how fast I drove, there was no end to the greyness. Thick clouds hung over the fields and trees stood alone at the edge of farms, far from shacks with slanted roofs ready to cave in. Something in my gut told me we'd never arrive at the cottage, and that feeling grew when Laurie got hungry. After waking up, she'd riffled through a packet of crisps but said it wasn't enough, and she craved something that wasn't like 'eating air'.

'Are you sure you can't wait?' I said. 'We'll be there in less than two hours.'

'I can't wait that long.' She let the empty crisps packet fly out the window.

'Really?'

'Is that you being testy, Albie?'

'Alright, I'll stop at a petrol station somewhere. Buy you a Snickers.'

'How romantic of you,' she said. 'A minging place like that to kick off our anniversary.'

'You forgot how we met?'

'Oh, come on, somewhere nicer. We didn't come all this way to eat at a fucking petrol station.'

I drove around forty miles till we found a diner. We both stared up at the plastic cow on the roof as we walked across the car park.

The smell of greasy bacon hit us at the entrance. Inside, shrieking children ran around, ducking and diving under their parents in the queue. Lone men drank coffee and tucked into rolls stuffed with brown shreds of bacon. Laurie chose a table by the window and slid a sticky menu across the table to me. I glanced at it then watched her scanning hers.

'What you having?' I said.

She dug inside her handbag. 'I don't know yet. I can't find my contacts. They must be in one of my other bags.'

'I'll get them later. Here.' I read out what they had. After a delay she went for a bacon roll.

'What about you?' Laurie said.

'I'm not hungry,' I said, getting up to join the queue.

I watched Laurie biting into her bacon roll. She ate like a wee bird wrestling a scrap of food too big for it. I could hear the grinding of her teeth as she crunched into the tough slabs. A cappuccino rested in my hands. I'd asked for a black coffee, but I didn't bother sending it back. It was a good prop.

Over Laurie's shoulder a hefty truck driver kept eyeballing me. Ketchup dripped from his chin, and in between bites of his roll he wheezed. The air in the place was stifling.

'Be back in a second,' I said.

Laurie murmured something through a full mouth.

It was a relief to step outside. I tried Kenny again. On the fifth ring he answered.

'Hello?'

'Kenny, there's a problem.'

'Problem?'

'Aye. Roger didn't turn up and—'

'He didn't turn up? You serious?'

'Aye.'

'Fuck sake.'

'And the guy, I've still got him with me. I've come all this way with Laurie and him in the fucking boot. What do I do?' I thought I heard laughter on his end.

'Is he out? The guy?'

I looked over at my Merc, half-expecting the boot to burst open. 'Aye. Well at least he was last time I checked. I gave him some sleeping pills.'

'Good thinking. How many?'

'The whole packet. You think that's enough?'

'Can I get some of that Cajun salt if you got it, hen?' Kenny said.

'Kenny?'

'What you saying, Al?'

'About the tablets. You think a whole pack's enough to put him out?' Again, more laughter, this time louder.

'Aye that should be fine.'

'Am I on speakerphone?' I said, looking back at the diner. I saw Laurie through the window, still scrapping with her bacon roll.

'What? Don't be daft,' Kenny said. 'I'm just out having a bite to eat. Where abouts are you?'

'We've stopped at a diner. Been driving over an hour. This is all fucking Roger's fault. I tell you when I see him, I'll—'

'Wait. Calm down, Al.' Kenny breathed in slowly as if he was the one who needed to relax. For a second it seemed like he wasn't going to exhale or speak again. 'Right, calm down, Al. I'll deal with Roger. You're going up north, right?'

'Aye, we're heading to a cottage.'

'Lovely. Cheers, hen. A cottage? They'll be secluded spots there. Distract your woman somehow. Make sure she stays inside. Give her one of those pills if you have to. Then drive somewhere quiet and deal with it.'

'But I just find them and send them to Roger. I've never—'

'It's Friday, Al. Just fucking deal with it.' Kenny hung up.

Back at our table Laurie had set aside her plate and was texting. The food had hardly been touched.

When we reached the car, she moved towards the boot.

'What you doing?' I said.

'I need to get my contacts from my bag remember. Hurry up and open.'

'But you don't need them now. You just ate.'

'I want to have a good look at the place when we get there.'

'Okay, I'll get them for you,' I said. She hopped in front of me and stood with her arms crossed and back against the boot.

'Why?'

'There's ... There's something in there I don't want you to see. Not yet. It's kind of a surprise.'

Laurie tried to stare me out. I raised a hand in peace. Her face lit up and she squealed. 'Oh, I wonder what it could be!' I guided her to the passenger seat and made sure she was strapped in.

A family parked next to us and I waited ages for them to step out and walk past. A wee girl buzzing to use her legs again darted about the car park screeching. She craned her head at me in a way that made me feel too visible. I stood up straight and smiled casually at her parents as they passed.

I opened the boot and reached under my shirt. The stink of stale piss burned in my nostrils. Baldie snored lightly in a foetal position, drool frothing from the corners of the tape. His broken specs had fallen to his chin. The old piss stains had dried, and I couldn't detect any fresh marks. It was hard to imagine what this guy had done to fuck Kenny off. Probably cheated at golf.

Laurie was sitting upright with her arms folded over her chest when I returned with her contacts.

'Here you go.' I held up the rectangular box, but she didn't move, just continued to stare ahead at the motorway.

'Everything good?'

She didn't answer. I dropped the box on her lap and turned on the engine. Whatever was coming could be dealt with somewhere else.

The light got weaker the further north we went. Rain spattered the windows, and neither of us had said a word. The only other noise came from Laurie's sighs, fast and irregular. At one point I put out my hand to turn on the radio, but she stopped me with her eyes. She was determined to take that atmosphere with us to the cottage.

'Alright Laurie, what's the matter?' I said at last.

She kept looking at the windshield wipers as if her thoughts had got lost somewhere in their swishing motion.

'I found your phone, Albert.'

I reached in my pocket. 'My phone's here.'

'Not that phone. Your other one.'

I felt heat surge through my body, the kind that blasts you when opening an oven.

'What's her name?' she said, waving the screensaver in my face.

I tightened my hands on the wheel. 'You went into the fucking glove compartment?'

Laurie didn't answer, just lit a fag.

I drove on in silence for maybe ten minutes. In that time, she'd exhausted all of the password attempts and flung the phone against the back seat.

I finally spoke after she'd inserted her contacts.

'Rachel's her name. She's my wife. But our relationship … it's not what it was. It's non-existent. She doesn't even know where I am. She doesn't care.'

Laurie's eyes sharpened. 'She doesn't care? Oh, I'm so sorry. That must be awful for you. Really fucking awful.' Her foot started up. 'I knew it. I just knew something would fuck up our anniversary. What else have you lied about? Do you even work in advertising?'

'Let's just get to where we're going and we'll sort things out. Just let me get there, please.' My voice broke as I said 'please' and she snorted.

'I can't believe this, I really can't. Going to the country with a married man.' She blew smoke in my face.

'Hey, that's not—' I heard a low groan escape above the lashing rain.

'That's not what? That's not what?'

I turned on the radio and cranked up the volume at the first station I found. 'Nothing,' I said. 'This is my tune.'

Laurie threw me a sidelong glance and said slowly, 'This is a news report, Albert.' We waited a few seconds as a woman rattled off a story about a missing sheep reunited with its flock after escaping during a thunderstorm.

'Well, it's a lovely story,' I said. I wiped my hand against my thigh then changed stations.

A dull thump sounded behind us. Laurie sat up and looked out the window. 'What was that?'

'What was what?' I fist-pumped at landing on some heavy metal tune and turned the knob all the way up. But the thump didn't come just once. More followed, harder and faster, as though we were under attack from snowballs. Laurie looked out again. Ash broke off the tip of her fag. She turned to me.

'It's just the music,' I said, keeping my hand over the knob. 'It's just the music.' Guttural moans joined in with the pounding from the boot. Laurie placed her hand over mine. I let her pull my fingers away. She turned off the radio. Through the soaked windshield the light had all but faded across the rolling green hills.

Equinox

A Heartfelt Request

——Emily Crawford——

Please, dance with me in the dark,

When voices have died and eyes have closed,

When all other lights have gone out,

Come with me to a world of dreams;

To a world unlike this one,

Where wonders leap from the walls

And fill the room with times gone by.

Let us dance aside the generals on their horses

Through fields of gold below Starry Nights,

Through the renaissance of creation to our Last Judgment,

For now, there is no way for them to know.

Trust in me as I in you.

All senses have dulled, and another light leads my way,

Lead me in this dance, be my guide.

Stay with me, and only me,

To share in a fleeting moment through the unknown

Where I will dance, if only to dance with you.

A Starlight Dance

—Emily Crawford—

AS MUCH AS IT PAINED her to admit it, he was right. The light of the sun had vanished, and the sky was black. There was no point trying to push through the night, though a point could have been made to find somewhere more comfortable to stay. The rotten timbers, crumbling stone, and dusted floors of the ruins he had picked were about as welcoming as the bitter draft blowing in from the open doorway.

Nymphara shivered, sitting on the edge of a broken chair as she watched him destroy what remained of the cottage's contents. Sifting through the limbs of tables and chairs and tearing the fabric of old upholstery, he constructed a fire in the centre of the room. He struck the back of his blade with a chipped cobble and set it ablaze. He was settling down for the evening, the glow of growing flames reflecting in the black plate of his armour as he doffed it. He was gentle with each piece he removed, and she was surprised at what lay beneath. He wasn't wrapped in dirty leathers or battered chainmail, instead he wore a noble's coat and tails and dusted off his jacket as he sat down by the fire.

They had travelled together for only a few days, and for all that time he had been cold. Even now in the heat of the fire he still seemed cold, but, in this light, Enoch seemed like a different man.

'What are you staring at?'

'Nothing.'

He raised an eyebrow. 'Okay, well, get some rest. I'll take watch again tonight, and we'll get on the road before daybreak. Hopefully someone there knows who you are.'

She clicked her heels together, watching as the dust and dirt fell from the soles.

'What's wrong?'

'I'm not tired,' she protested.

'You might not be, but we have a long journey ahead of us tomorrow, so sleep.'

'But I can't.'

'Then find some way to entertain yourself. Make yourself tired.'

She hopped from the chair with a sudden spring in her step and a grin on her face. 'Dance with me?'

'What?'

'Will you dance with me?'

'No.'

'Why not? Scared?'

'I have never danced before. If you wish to dance, dance on your own.'

'You want me to get tired, you want me to rest,' she pouted, 'so dance with me, Enoch. It'll be fun.'

'Fun?'

She had heard enough. She marched across the floor towards him and grabbed hold of his wrist, struggling as she tried to pull him to his feet. 'Come on,' she strained, 'get up already.'

'Fine …' He stood up, lifting his arm and letting her dangle there for a moment or two before setting her down on the ground. 'What now?'

'Arms out.'

The pressed folds of his jacket creased. Its crisp silhouette wrinkled. He stood in front of her like a scarecrow, arms out and legs together. The ruffles of his collar even puffed up around his neck like bundled haylage. He was rigid. Static and stiff as he waited for his next instruction.

Nymphara shook her head and laughed. She had seen him slay drakes and dragons, those bandits on the mountain side, and yet this was what scared him. 'Try to relax, Enoch. It's not going to kill you, it's just a dance.'

He didn't respond. He stood motionless and silent. She couldn't take the smile off her face. There was a part of her that was revelling in his embarrassment.

She reached backward towards her pack and with wisps of magic, pulled her harp from its confines. She flicked her wrist, twisting the magic as if she were conducting an orchestra. She twitched her fingers, and the wisps began to pluck the strings. Truly enchanted, she left her magic to play the music as she took the appropriate stance. She raised her left arm to meet the height of his shoulder and held out her right hand for him to hold. She stretched, balancing on the balls of her feet as she rose to meet his gaze. 'Take a step forward, take my hand, and put the other around my waist.'

There was no fluidity to it. His arms almost cracked as they bent into position. Like claws, his fingers dug into her back and curled around her hand. She became stuck in the crease of his elbow and felt the tension squeeze.

The twang of the harp strings echoed, frightening several of the birds nesting in the rafters. They fled from the house. The creaking timbers and battering of their wings drowned out by her sudden screams.

'Enoch, not so tight!'

She twisted her hips and tried to wriggle from his grasp.

He didn't panic, but he did let go. Enoch took a step back and left her be.

Flexing her fingers, Nymphara inspected her hand. It had lost any semblance of colour and a few red marks dented the skin, but it didn't feel broken. Her back on the other side ached. It felt like something was missing, as if he had accidently ripped something out as she wormed her away from his grasp. She took a breath.

'I think … maybe that's enough for tonight.'

'No.'

'What?'

'No,' Enoch repeated, 'I wish to try again.'

'Enoch, I don't think …'

She straightened up and saw him waiting for her. He stood with his shoulders straight and an arm behind his back. He was still rigid and stiff. Like dry grass, it looked like a soft breeze would be enough to knock him off balance and snap him in half. Extending his left hand, he gave a slight bow.

'I wish to try again.'

She turned away, casting her eyes to the sky and then to the fire. The melodies of the harp rose above the crackling flames. It had corrected itself and returned to playing its tune. The shock didn't break her concentration. It was still bewitched, playing what she wanted it to because she wanted it to.

Nymphara looked back at him and gave a weak smile. She was hesitant, but she took his hand and stepped into position. Enoch did too, raising her hand in his and placing the other on her waist. His grip was still tight, but she could feel him tense as he restrained his uncertainty.

'Relax, Enoch. Just follow my lead.'

She stepped left and he followed robotically. She took a step back to the centre and felt the metal of his sabatons brush against her bare foot. Nymphara swallowed. Each movement she made was making her as nervous as him. She stopped.

'Enoch, you need to relax.'

His grip tightened. It did every time she told him to relax. It was instinctual rather than impulsive, as if he was doing it without a thought. It was a twitch, the tick of a child who had just gotten into trouble. He wasn't getting frustrated at her; he was becoming frustrated with himself.

'Enoch,' she said, trying to soften her tone with a sigh, 'close your eyes.'

'What? Why would I do that?'

'Just trust me, okay? Close your eyes and just listen to the music.'

'Nymphara, this is ridiculous.'

'You were the one who wished to try again, so do what I'm telling you to do and close your eyes.'

His eyes rolled, but he obliged. He sighed. 'What now?'

'Now lead.'

'What?'

'Enoch.'

'How do I lead with my eyes closed?'

'Listen to the music. Now shut up and lead.'

'Fine, fine … fine.'

They stood still for a time, or at least he did. Nymphara quickly started to fidget. She tapped her toes and knocked her knees together. She rapped her fingers against his shoulder in time with the harp. She did anything that she could, locked in his grasp.

And then he took a breath.

The white frost escaped his lips and froze the air between them. A sudden dusting of the tiniest snowflakes fluttered down and stuck to her hair, each one twinkling like stars in the light of the fire. They melted in the heat, and Enoch started to move.

At first, he only swayed, moving her from left to right without picking his feet up from the floor. But then he stepped forward, forcing her to step back. He stepped right and she was suddenly pulled the same way. He stayed within the cracks of the cobbles beneath their feet, careful never to touch them or cross them. His movements were gentle and fluid, and soon she found his rhythm.

She followed his steps and looked up to meet his gaze. His eyes were still closed, but his head had tilted as if to look down at her. It was hard to know for sure as his cheeks had become flush with colour, but she could almost swear he was smiling.

She gasped.

Enoch suddenly spun her out, extending an arm and leading her around him as she turned on her heel. The hem of her skirt kicked up the dust and ash which had gathered from the fire. The wisps of smoke trailed around her as each speck started to spark. They followed her as Enoch pulled her in close and continued his waltz.

He danced around the room and the sparks ignited. Flames were dancing with them, licking at the floor and singeing the edges of his jacket and her dress. She could feel their warmth but not their heat. With each spin, they climbed high and illuminated the spectacle. With each step, they settled and dulled. Never did they burn her. She was safe in his grasp.

The sounds of her harp rose as she felt her heart flutter. Nymphara closed her eyes and became lost in their moment. She let herself drift with the cinders, high into the starry sky and into the night. They were dancing on air, waltzing through the heavens. Enoch was a different man.

She felt herself swoon, and she felt him stop. She opened her eyes and her harp clattered to the ground.

Enoch dipped her, arching her back as he shifted his weight forward. He was so close. He had followed in a shallow bow. She could feel his breath cold on her neck. He was too close.

Nymphara panicked. She threw herself forward, ducking under his chin and pushing herself against his chest. She knocked him off balance, causing him to stumble as she woke him from his trance.

His eyes were wide as he looked at her. 'Nymphara?'

'You're a pretty good dancer,' she laughed nervously, letting go of him completely and quickly going to tend to her harp.

'Nymphara?'

A few of its strings had snapped, but it was nothing she couldn't fix. She started to fiddle with it, trying to ignore him.

'Nymphara?'

He was persistent.

'Yes, Enoch?'

'I'd like to do that again.'

A lump was caught in the back of her throat and turned her stomach. She tried to swallow. Instead, she coughed, choking as she tripped over her words. 'It's late, but you say we'll arrive in town tomorrow, yeah? We could go to a tavern, they'll be sure to have music, and I'm sure there'll be plenty of people who would have you dance with them.'

She had set the harp aside and started to pace. She avoided him, hurriedly walking around the other side of the fire to reach her bedroll.

Enoch hadn't moved. He was frozen, staring at his empty hands.

'Enoch, it's late,' she said, hoping to wake him once more. 'We should get some rest.'

He looked up. 'Nymphara?'

'Yes, Enoch?'

'I'd like to do that again,' he repeated. 'With you.'

Kleine Maus

—— *Matthew Weston* ——

THUNDER RUMBLED ACROSS THE SKY. Grey clouds hung over Uhrmacherstadt. Lightning flashed and illuminated the black silhouette of the fortress above the town. Greta shivered beneath the blankets of her bed. She had tried to distract herself from the noise of the storm, counting brush strokes through her hair. It did not help. Instead, she was drawn to counting the seconds between each flash of lightning and crack of thunder.

Flash ... one, two, three, four ... crack.

The other children had heard there would be a storm and decided to frighten her. It was the first time she had been told the story of Festung Uhrwerkherz. Greta had not wanted to burden her mother and father with the tormenting words of the children. She was accustomed to their taunts, and felt it was all her own fault. Her fingers scratched across the itch on her palm.

Flash ... one, two, three ... crack.

The storm was getting closer, rain was hammering against the roof. Hundreds upon hundreds of watery missiles lay siege to the home that felt so flimsy compared to the fortress. Her mind refused to calm. Greta tried again to distract it. Her father's brown leather coat had seven silver buttons, the clock-tower square had four willow trees in it, there were nine Ältermannen on the town council.

Flash ... one, two ... crack.

It was nearly upon her now. Her entire body trembled. The children had frightened her with tales of clockwork monsters defending the fortress. Greta could not push the images out of her mind. Squeezing her eyes shut, she tried again to escape into the simplicity of numbers. She was seven years old; she had seen twenty-eight seasons; she had lived through three hundred and sixty-seven weeks. She reached for anything to count.

Flash ... one ... crack.

Greta screamed, pulling the blankets over her head. Her breathing was rapid and unsteady. Her mind was filled with visions of twisted shadows and clockwork claws. She could hear the ticking of mechanical monsters as they drew closer and closer. Her thoughts would not turn away from the fortress. It was as though its shadow was smothering her. Seven silver buttons, four willow trees, nine Ältermannen, seven years old, twenty-eight seasons, three hundred and sixty-seven weeks ...

Crack ... flash.

She screamed once more. The storm was above her. It was all around her, there could be no escape. No numbers could draw her mind from the fear. It was overwhelming. She felt a shift on the side of her bed and screamed again.

'Greta, it's alright. It's me,' her mother's voice spoke softly. Greta opened her eyes, slowly pulling back her blankets from over her head. Her mother sat on the edge of the bed, a flickering candle held in one hand. Greta watched her place it upon the bedside table before pulling her into her arms. The hug was like a warm blanket, keeping her safe even as her mother's nightshirt grew damp beneath Greta's eyes. Her mother ran gentle hands through Greta's hair, making soothing, shushing noises as her daughter's shoulders shook. The storm raged on outside, but her mother's presence held its anger at bay. Greta could still feel the looming silhouette of her thoughts, but as long as her mother was here it did not matter.

'What is wrong, mein kind?'

Greta shook her head. She could not tell her mother. She would not be a burden. Their family was avoided in Uhrmacherstadt. Her father was forced to keep his clocks hidden away in his workshop. He would share his passion with Greta, but never with anyone else. The Bürgermeister did nothing to prevent the insults thrown at her family. Greta would not add to their problems. Her mother squeezed her closer, gently kissing her head, holding her while the storm continued. Her mother was so comforting, and it was hard not to confide in her. While Greta shared a passion for

71

clockwork with her father, her tiny hands guided by his when working together, her mother had given her the gift of numbers. It was her greatest escape from her troubles.

'The storm ...' Greta murmured, pressing her face deeper into her mother's chest, 'I am scared of the storm.' Inside she cringed, wishing she could explain further. Her mother was quiet for a long moment, running her hand through Greta's hair. It was something that Greta could focus on, something she could count. Her mother had never commented on her daughter's quirks, she always accepted that was how Greta approached the world. It was a passion they shared, a talent for numbers. Greta was happy that her mother knew her in a way no one else did, that her mother could join her in adoration of the simplest calculations. Her mother understood.

'You were told the story weren't you, mein kind?' her mother eventually asked. Greta did not need to answer but nodded anyway. Her mother hummed softly and planted another gentle kiss on her daughter's head.

'Is it the storm that scares you Greta, or the clockwork creatures?' It was an insightful question. The storm was a cover for the creeping clockwork creatures that really terrified her. It was a corruption of her father's passion. While he specialised in building clocks, after Greta was born, he started to make clockwork toys. She had soldiers she could wind up and watch march, and music boxes that mimicked the motions of musicians. The monsters of the fortress were so far from these pieces of passion-filled art that it terrified her. Her mother knew this already, and Greta did not need to speak. That was something that made her mother special to Greta and her father. Her mother would simply understand them.

'Would you like to hear another story, mein kind?' The question surprised Greta, and she took a moment to realign the cogs of her mind. She pulled back, sniffing away the tears and staring up into the soft smile. She barely noticed the storm anymore.

'A story?'

'Yes, a story about the lonely clockmaker, the merchant's daughter, and the kleine maus.' Greta settled back into the comforting embrace, restarting the count of her mother's strokes through her hair. One, two, three ...

'Once upon a time,' her mother began, using her storyteller's voice that Greta loved, 'there was a lonely clockmaker. He lived in a house down a little lane nestled between a blacksmith and a coffin-maker. He lived alone because his parents had sent him away from their home as no one in the town trusted a clockmaker. They refused to see his kind heart.'

The candlelight flickered and the rain continued to hammer on the roof. Greta pictured her father, his shaggy brown hair tied neatly back as he bent over his workshop table, neatly cut pieces of wood and crafted cogs set precisely in order as he put them together. He worked alone, and she was certain he would never leave his workshop if not for her mother. It made her sad to think of a lonely clockmaker with no one to call family. She knew her father was always kind, even to those who openly insulted him. He had told her that it cost him nothing to be kind to those who disliked him, but it lost them their dignity. It was hard to see the townsfolk turn against him as he simply smiled back at them. She wished other children could gain as much joy as she did from the toys he crafted.

'People shunned the lonely clockmaker because the Baron had once tinkered with clockwork devices, before bargaining with a demon to construct his fortress.

'Living in the town was a merchant's daughter, the seventh child of a family with six sons. Her father would often travel, taking one or more of her brothers along with him, but he would always leave her to manage his market stall. She was the most beautiful woman in town, her curling hazel hair framing a heart shaped face with chocolate brown eyes. Many young suitors hoped to win her hand, but she rebuffed them all. She did not want to marry someone who saw her as a prize, instead wanting a partner to love her for who she was. The clockmaker adored her from afar, enchanted by her fiery joy in life and sharp wit, piercing the egos of pompous young men. However, he was never brave enough to speak to her.'

Greta wondered if this story was real. Was it about her father and mother? She did not wish to ask and interrupt the gentle flow of her mother's story. They were quite different when speaking. Greta would often get tongue-tied before slipping into silence, but Mother was always brimming with life and something to say. Secretly Greta thought that she had been the one to ask her father to marry, as it was hard to picture him being so bold.

'In fact, the lonely clockmaker did not speak much at all, except when he had to converse with merchants or those few who would ask for his help. He spoke as quietly as a little mouse squeaked. The townsfolk called him the clockwork mouse, and children would often squeak and giggle as he walked by.'

Greta knew all too well how mean children could be. They would laugh and tell her to count things, adding or taking items away to throw her off. They asked if she was alive or just a clockwork doll made by her father. She knew that mean children could grow into horrible adults.

'One night the clockmaker cried himself to sleep in his workshop. The townspeople had gathered wherever he went, old and young all squeaking as he ran his errands. He was glad to see that the merchant's daughter was not involved. In his slumber, he did not notice a little mouse scampering up his chair and onto his worktable. Earlier that day he had finished a fine cuckoo clock, all it was missing was the tweeting bird. The little mouse clambered onto the top of the clock. She was as lonely as the clockmaker because she had also lost her family. The townsfolk forced them out of their homes for fear of disease. This was particularly sad because the little mouse had a special talent: she could sing as beautifully as any bird. But people saw her as an annoyance and were scared of her gift.'

Greta smiled sadly. She understood how that mouse must have felt, feeling like there was no one but your family who would understand and care for you, that your special gift was an abnormality. She snuggled closer into her mother hoping the story would have a happy ending. If it was about her parents, she knew it did.

'The mouse began to sing softly, the anger of the townsfolk having driven her voice into a quiet whisper too, but as she sang her voice grew stronger and stronger. Her song was sweet and sad. The clockmaker was slowly roused from his sleep and was stunned to hear the little singing mouse. She had seen how the townsfolk treated the lonely clockmaker and how, when he had returned to his workshop, his tears had overflowed. The mouse was also a kind-hearted soul and could not see someone cry without trying to help. That was why she had climbed on his worktable.'

It was hard to listen to the tale of these two sad souls, so connected in their loneliness.

Her mother began to hum a soft tune. Greta was only just able to hear it over the strong winds and torrential rain. It was slow and melodic, like her mother's storytelling voice. The candle had almost burned down, leaving just a small flickering light illuminating her small room. Greta could almost hear the little mouse's sad song. She could imagine her father lifting his head from the table to witness this magical sight, and the joy it brought him.

'The little mouse paused as she saw the clockmaker watching her. "Go on kleine maus," he said quietly. "Please keep singing." The little mouse puffed up with pride and continued her song. Her voice was now strong and joyful.

'The clockmaker and the mouse shared stories of their lives. The little mouse spoke of her family with so many brothers and sisters who had been forced to go their separate ways. The clockmaker spoke of his growing love for the merchant's daughter and his fear of rejection.

'However, the lonely clockmaker was not the only one to hear the little mouse. The merchant's daughter was passing his home when she heard the beautiful song. She stopped to listen, enchanted by the melody. She considered knocking on the door and inquiring about the music, but she was scared. Instead, she stayed until the singing stopped and the sun had set. The clockmaker thanked the little mouse and said she could live in his cuckoo clock, and he would provide her meals if she would sing for him to ease his loneliness. She accepted and so they lived, the clockmaker crafting clocks while the mouse sang sweet songs.

'Neither of them knew that every evening the merchant's daughter would stand outside their home listening raptly. Sometimes she would move close to the door and raise her hand to knock, but she was always too afraid of what the clockmaker might say, the fear of rejection overwhelming her longing to know. Every night the same sweet song would come from the clockmaker's home, and for weeks and weeks she stood outside listening. One night as she was leaving, she stumbled and fell against the door with a loud thump. The little mouse stopped singing and the clockmaker looked up from his work. He stood and slowly made his way to the door. The merchant's daughter had only just righted herself when he opened it. They both stood frozen in fear, uncertain what they should do next.'

Greta imagined a younger version of her mother and father caught in a moment of awkwardness. She could picture the embarrassed flush on her mother's cheeks, and the mussed-up hair of her father. There was a sweetness to it that made her smile.

'Eventually the merchant's daughter plucked up courage and asked, "Who sings so sweetly here every night?" The lonely clockmaker was unsure how to answer, his little mouse had told him how badly the townsfolk had treated her. He was uncertain how the lovely merchant's daughter would react to his sweet little mouse. "She is very shy," he said softly, "I do not know if she would sing with you here." The merchant's daughter nodded and asked "Could I listen inside? Your friend need not see me." The clockmaker thought for a moment then replied, "I shall ask my little friend and see what she thinks." The clockmaker returned to his workshop, finding the mouse perched on her cuckoo clock. "Kleine Maus," he said, "there is someone here who wishes to hear you sing." The little mouse shrank in on herself uncertainly. "But I am shy," she squeaked, "and what if they are afraid of me?" The clockmaker crouched before the little mouse, his eyes level with her own. "If they do not like you for who you are," he said, his voice gentle but firm, "then they are not welcome in my home." The mouse was clever and saw there was more to what the clockmaker was saying so she asked, "Who wants to hear my song?" The clockmaker blushed and the little mouse knew immediately. "I shall sing for her," she declared with a wavering squeak. "Perhaps she might see you for the kind-hearted man I know you to be."'

Her mother paused once more. Greta was now so focused on the tale the storm did not matter.

'Please, go on,' she yawned, finally relaxed but refusing to sleep until she knew the end of the story.

'Very well, mein kind,' her mother replied, amused. 'Let me get more comfortable.'

They shuffled around on her bed until her mother was sat resting against the headboard and Greta's head lay comfortably in her lap. Her mother's hands returned to her hair, gently stroking each curl.

'The clockmaker ushered the merchant's daughter into his home, instructing her to stay at the door to his workshop. There she would be hidden but able to see through the crack. At first, she was confused not seeing another person or any contraption that could be the source of such sweet songs. Then she spotted the little mouse perched on top of the cuckoo clock. She was scared, as many are of mice, but then the mouse began to sing. She started softly, barely louder than a squeak, but as she relaxed her voice grew and grew. The merchant's daughter was as enchanted as the clockmaker at the talented little mouse. Then she noticed the finished clocks all around, grand cuckoo clocks with feather-laden designs, ornate mantle clocks with smooth curves and round edges, and simple little clocks with white faces and pitch-black hands. They were all works of art. The grandest of all was a longcase clock, as tall as her and then some, carved from regal oak, with a long brass pendulum etched with fine scrolls of silver filigree.'

Greta knew all those clocks. They were her father's pride and joy. People who bought clocks from him were rare, but they always appreciated the dedication put into each piece.

'The merchant's daughter realised that the little mouse was not the only one gifted in this home. "Oh, kleine maus, thank you," she said stepping into the workshop and smiling at the little mouse as tears formed, "you have opened my eyes." The lonely clockmaker smiled, happy to see his friend receiving such praise. The merchant's daughter then turned to him. "And thank you, Herr Clockmaker," she continued, "you took in this wonder when others would have driven her out. This town does not deserve your kind heart." From then on, the merchant's daughter and the clockmaker became close friends, eventually courting and marrying, and the little mouse lived with them until her dying day.'

Greta's eyelids had grown heavy and the fog of sleep was slowly beginning to claim her. She had to know though.

'Was father the lonely clockmaker and were you the merchant's daughter?' she mumbled.

'We were,' her mother answered, her voice full of nostalgia, 'and now you are our special gifted Kleine Maus, Greta.'

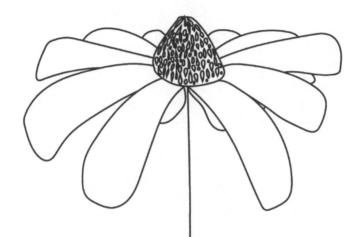

SPRING

SPRING

Oneness (Haiku)

—Marianne L. Berghuis—

rippled wave
retreats
undivided from the
deep soothing
silver orb

The Ither Pandemic

——Marianne L. Berghuis ——

There's a pandemic gaun oan
But it's nae the wan yer thinking.
Aye, coronavirus maks us feart,
But it's oor mental minds that're sinkin'.

Oor race thrives oan human contact.
We're a truly social kind o' breed,
But ye cannae gie a bosie tae a laptop,
So, oan oor ain thochts we start tae feed.

Feeling trapped an' jist richt scunnered
Wi' nae end tae social isolation.
Nae bletherin' doon the club hoose,
An' thon *'Zoom'*, it's o' fek aw consolation.

Aye, it's anither kind o' pandemic,
But it's aboot oor mental health decline.
So, let's find weys tae support each other,
An' no say…'Acht, ma heid's jist richt an' fine.'

Come oan… get oot yer fower wa'd prison
An' goan in tae nature for a daunder.

Look aboot ye, tak in aw the bonnie things
As ye walk up an' oar the hillside yonder!

An' when yer feeling doonricht low
To yersel' be really, truly kind
Jist pause…breathe, in an' oot, an'
Look aifter yer ane wee precious mind.

Spring Day Lockdown

——David Topliff——

Cawing rooks and crows
Slice and glide the warm airwaves
Drowning out old dogs

Fast clouds sail like leaves
In the gentle blue-sky breath
Wispy soft and dry
Colours turn to green again
With promises of berries

Flying bug buzzes
Laughing ice cream memories
Absent traffics gift

Following Up

——David Topliff——

I dreamed I sold
An expensive poem
Then good God
The phone would not stop ringing

Singing to the shop
I bought my long-suffering wife
A gold ring
A rare paid for surprise

I got laid and
The council tax was paid
Had a takeaway
And another the next day

They fawned, oh man
Do it just the same again
To please them
I gave them this one.

Summer Lawns

——David Topliff——

Should jumpers be quickly tossed
Shoes off and socks
Under used deck chairs
Usually buried in dark sheds
Miracles suggest indulgence
Maybe a mojito
Easily lying still
Eating hours like crisps
Radio repetitions
Relishing summer loves

Let's not care for business
Landlines can ring out
As-and-whens collecting
Aspirations melting
Wear what one wants to
Where what one wants
Now and now alone
Naked rest.
Simple and probably
Short

Route Map

——David Topliff——

Starting Out

THE WONDERS OF THE SCOTTISH West Coast are not to be underestimated. Neither are its hazards. Many a hiker, day-tripper, and experienced hill climber have been caught out by drastic and sudden changes in the weather or by underestimating the hidden perils of some of the most innocent looking trails. The ground can be wet and unstable. Help can be difficult to find. Wear sturdy boots and layers of suitable clothing. It is always a good idea to carry a basic first aid kit. The Scottish Outdoor Access Code should be followed at all times. Ramblers should adhere to its instructions regarding dogs and livestock.

Kendis, do you remember how pleased we were to finally be starting our adventure? I know you said that staying with my folks in Jedburgh was okay, but I knew it wasn't. They didn't get you. I told you they would think you were gangster. You laughed and said that, in that case, London was a lot like Jedburgh. If you were upset, you put it all into your art. Here is one I reckon you wrote on the train over to the west coast to finally start our walk.

> *First steps can be hard*
> *Rhythm must be established*
> *Boots get broken in*

So that was you predicting the future. You and your bloody boots. I said not to buy new ones just before a long walk, but you just sucked your teeth in a wry parody of your mum.

Looking back over the other stuff you wrote in that early part of our walk I am a wee bit annoyed by how messy your pencilled handwriting is. I am not going back over your words with a biro, like you would have done. I will put my neat notes at the edges of this notebook or on clean sheets of paper that I can glue on, also like you would have done. I will attach the cut-up bits of the walker's guide and write out some of the clearer poems I can discern. I won't touch your awesome cartoons.

Clachan Bridge to Soroba Hill.

It is hard to imagine a more classic west highland walk than the Fa'n Dacker Way. Begin southwest from Oban at the way mark at Clachan Bridge. The path leads along the coast before veering south over the high ground up Soroba Hill. At the peak it drops down to the west and flattens out. Later, there will be signs of modern life, but in this first section, one can visit a landscape that is little changed by time or man. The downward path to the moor can be steep and difficult, particularly after wet weather.

I like this one. I hear your voice like you are thinking out loud and that helps when I can't read your handwriting.

> *I am better with roads than paths.*
> *Odd streets and even crossing lanes,*
> *Lines with no signs*
> > *We trek like drovers.*

I don't know how much to put in this book. Your mum died. Or do you know that? Your dad went kind of mad for a bit. I went to see him a few weeks after the funeral hoo-ha was over and he could barely speak. We just sat looking out of your front room window with him holding my hand and crying. I started going every other day. Now, all these years later, he isn't just your dad to me anymore. He is proper family.

A couple of weeks ago, at our irregular Sunday tea as he calls it, he presented me with all your old travel collages. He said he couldn't throw them out and that they belonged at mine. It was your school trip to Paris and your lad's week away in Seville and your trip to Malawi with your cousin in 2008 just before I met you. You had cleaned up the older ones and turned them into proper booklets. All the bits of travel guides and bus tickets and the best of your poems and sketches were all craftily glued together. Your art still smelled of your sense and, looking through it, I wanted to touch you again or to feel your breath on my neck. I hadn't felt that way in years.

I found these scraps in a plastic bag pushed in amongst your finished works. Your mum probably found it in your bag and couldn't bare it, stuffing it out of mind. I can't write like you. I can't put words in your silent mouth. All I can do is save these loose pages from languishing in a forgotten bag and try to finish your story for you.

Soroba Hill to Ardfern

The route continues through the glen. The way descends through fields of mulling sheep before a series of short ascents which can test even experienced walkers. This path should be adhered to at all times but especially during lambing season. Your hard work will be rewarded when you ascend again to the pretty village of Naesae. It has B and B accommodation, and the campground has a shop and pub.

> *This is not that.*
> *Choose*
> *One way must be followed.*
> *Walk or just wait.*
> *Turn*
> *To tell three paths apart.*
> *Time changes step.*
> *Pause*
> *To practice patience*
> *Through unfair rain.*
> *Count*
> *Long days with wet hands.*

You wrote this after we had that big fight that cleared the air and made us both realise that we were smart to come on this adventure. If we had just stayed in Brixton, trying to steer our new love through our old routes, who knows what deal we would have struck, if any. Remember going to that party and meeting Damon

Albarn? You two chatting all night like old pals? You would have mixed tracks and wrote lyrics and slid between all the other cool dudes. But really, you would never make it without my help. You needed someone to care enough to be honest with you.

When, knee deep in the Scottish mud, we had that barney, I realised that we could fight. We *would* fight. But you loved me, and you listened to me and knew when I talked sense. After the shouting we walked for an hour without talking and that was okay too.

Sparks

We are sparks,
Millisecond illuminations
From a blazing
Consuming flame.
We fly the firelight
Quick cooling, celestial
As shimmering brief
Wee Orions.
We float into the night,
Fluid as a former love
Waiting for the life
Beyond our ken.

It's funny going back after all these years. The shop looks the same with its Tunnock's Tea Cakes and plastic bottles of Skin So Soft. It had plenty of plasters for your boot rubbed heels. The walker's guide glorified that tatty pub with its tinny tasting Tennent's and those gross little packets of pork scratchings that you absolutely loved.

Here we finally relaxed. We hung our soaking tent and dried our sleeping bags in the bothie. We were so glad to drape our thick wet socks over the radiator, our soaking boots leaned up against it. When we did put them back on, they were warm and mostly dry. Remember how much we loved their shitty coffee that we didn't have to make? Oh, and toast from a toaster and warm bacon for you - eggs for me.

The travel guides are missing for the last part of our trek. They will still be in the original travel book because you never had the chance to snip them out. I have no idea where that has gone. I will try and fill in the missing bit.

Ardfern to Ellenabeich via Fairy Tree Hill

From here the path will take you downhill towards the sea. This section is the most dangerous in the trip and care should be taken, particularly after wet weather. Towards the end of the trail, where a wide plain is broken by the sheer drop down to near sea level, beware of sudden gusts of wind. But first, after the remoteness of the previous sections, it is nice to rest and play a bit. Lore tells us that this near junction of two burns that feed into the River Ugh is a symbol of frustrated young love. For years, new couples have been visiting the site to leave their hopes for their affairs on sheets of cloth hung from the branches of the local trees.

Be careful to rest here with your lover. Take time to appreciate the way the light bounces off their hair, or their eyes in the late twilight of June. Recall that couples have come before you to make their plans and firm their bonds. Linger in love's warm caress. Instead of rushing through, why not stay an extra night in the B and B?

That extra day was the best day of the whole adventure. We were both tired and between my sore legs and your manky feet, we were a mess. You were waxing eloquent about the wonderful civilising effects of a hot shower. I organised my stuff while you put the beginning of this book together. Then we lay silently on the bed for ages, revelling in being indoors in the daytime. You took my hand and we burst, without a word, into a long slow kiss. You had a new touch. We felt like each other's right choice. Your gentle strength combined perfectly with your beautiful attention to my detail. Your love. I remember wanting that night to last forever.

As we set out the next day, I was thinking that it all looked bright for us. You would never be the bloke I thought I wanted. How could you be? But you could have been my motor and I could have been your steering wheel. We would both trade in some of our old bad habits and learn some new ones together.

The Trail to Ellenabeich

This is the most ironic part of the walk. From the Fairy Tree the footpath takes walkers through a level plane that can be muddy, especially in spring when runoff has soaked the ground. Ramblers with good boots should have no trouble. There is an interesting set of standing stones halfway through the flatter part of this section. Most of these Neolithic monuments are put in locations that were auspicious to the original builders, normally with some sort of vista. This unusual sequence of stones grow in size every few hundred feet as they bring walkers nearer to the cliffs at Ellenabeich.

Danger. Now walkers must take particular caution. As the path comes to the cliff's edge it gives one of the best sea views in Scotland. It is stunning with its sheer drop down to the town of Ellenabeich. Follow the path carefully along the cliff edge and enjoy the vista before heading down a series of switchbacks that will bring you safely to the amenities in the pretty coastal town.

If you are tempted to stand near the sheer edge where the ground is often unreliable, be very cautious about where you put sore feet. Certainly, do not take off your boots to give those feet a break. Certainly, do not decide, no matter how your girlfriend implores you, to stand near the edge to take a selfie for the lads back home. Whatever you do, do not lean backwards to try and catch the sheer drop down to the village below in the picture. Never trust that the wind will be constant or that keeping your bare feet on the grass will mean you are safe.

Bunched up thoughts rescued from a corner,
Washed and dried, pressed and hung,
Tried on again at last,
Don't fit the same.
Have we grown?
Or shrank?
Yes!

There is a barrier now that separates walkers from the steep edge where you fell. It is bolted to the side of the cliff and supports a conveniently positioned information plaque. From this vista, the last place on earth you ever stood, I can see all the way down to the town where I will meet my family. I strain my eyes, but I can't make any of them out. The daughter you didn't even know had come into existence is with her brother and their dad. They've taken a little ferry over to that island just off the mainland. I can linger on high ground for a few minutes.

One day, when I've got it bound up and wrapped properly, this will be the guidebook for Maya when she wants to know about her birth dad. You've never been a secret, but she has forgotten the times we have talked about you and recently, I can see the toggles in her mind. She knows that her skin is darker than the rest of the family's. She knows that Harry is her only daddy but that she has three grandads. By the way, your dad dotes on both my kids. He is more gentle with them than I know he ever was with you. Ain't that the way of it?

She is beautiful, our daughter. She is the first to come to the aid of a classmate. She loves all animals, even the grumpy ones. Like you, she has a way of making a mark with a pencil that is both simple and elegant. I don't know if you know these things, wherever you are. She definitely has your sense of humour. I once famously caught her telling off the ice cream man for charging extra for the cone when she didn't even want it. The laughing man gave her the whole ice cream for free. She was only seven.

Maya will want to know why you fell. I will tell her that you slipped but I doubt that will satisfy her. There is no why. You slid silently into our past. Full stop. I will tell her how beautiful you were, with her eyes and your own mother's pecan skin. We will all talk about it as a family. I will give her these books. I will sing her your favourite songs.

I found out I was pregnant with Maya before the enquiry into your death was finished. I cried when I got both bits of news. Accidental death seemed too short a summary of your passing. I had known I was pregnant for a good month by then. I called my mum and dad and cried at them for an hour. Then I called your mum and dad and did it all again. By the time I went to bed, all cried out, I knew that I wanted Maya. I wanted her for myself. I wanted her to be the living memory of you. I loved you, Ken. I still do and always will.

Descent

This final part of the walk takes you down the paths that the sailors' wives would have climbed up to look out to the far ends of the sea to get some sign of their loved ones returning to the harbour. On boats that were loaded with fish or seals. With men tired of each other and biscuits and the work. There's no use standing there now. Kendis cannot come home.

You always used to say that all couples were about combinations and that we worked because you were the words and I was the numbers. If you had dreams, I wanted strategy. You took delight in the fine details while I couldn't take my mind off the big picture. I still can't. Harry is like me, but he is the algebra to my arithmetic. He tells our kids the stories, I make our plans. Never worry, Ken. He loves Maya like she is his own and she feels the same about him.

Going Further

From here you can pick up the coastal path which runs down the west coast for a further eighteen miles. Alternatively, you could meet your family when they get back from their ferry trip to that little island there. You can get in the car with the now finished chapter of a life not lived. You can go home. You're lucky. Tomorrow, you can drive across the country to stay with your parents and let them spoil your kids while you and Harry visit some of your old friends and have a proper catch up.

Now I walk the path that you never took and never will. You would have liked this bit. For one thing it is fast in the way that downhill walks are. The foliage changes from Gorse to Pearlwort and you would have liked that, collecting bits for your book. We probably would have finished by taking phone photos that you would print off later and paste into this, the last Kendis Route Map. I will do it for you. You would have liked the sense of achievement that comes at the end of a long walk. You would have waxed on about our pilgrimage to all our friends.

I don't linger at the bit where you hit the ground. After ten years you'd think I could bear it. But that is a step too far. I am amazed that I am here at all.

Maya, I will make a map to the exact spot where your father came to rest and you can come one day, if you want. I am sitting here now on the bench that marks the beginning of the walk from this side. I will just wait by this sandy beach for my family. It's getting late and we still have to drive back to our hotel and fish and chips in Oban.

Passing Tannery Way

—*Ashleigh Marie Symms*—

Where old oaks grow
thick and roads wind
upward, towards the evening sky,
we climb higher
and higher up the hill
along past Tannery Way.

Macadam roads merge
into dirt paths
and steep lopsided fields
as we trek through the silver birches,
just beginning
to grow green once again.

Sweet daffodils poke buds
through deep moist mud.
We flatten our path by trampling grass,
and as the track forks,
clamber through a rocky gap
to follow the gorse-lined trail.

Conifers cast shadows
across a burnt orange sky.
We reach the top
as the sun sets.
The air is cool now,
sharp to breathe.

Blades of grass
stick to the white tops
of my Converse
and dew droplets seep
through the canvas
into my socks.

Skeins of greylag fly
overhead through huddles of pinkish clouds.
You copy them, honking
and mimicking their wingbeat.
Laughing through heavy breaths,
side by side, skin touching skin,
we stand at the summit
of our world.

Tartan Pyjamas

—Ashleigh Marie Symms—

THERE'S MOULD GROWING ON OUR mattress. I changed the sheets yesterday. It's been a while since I last did it. Now little patches of pink and off-white-coloured stains have appeared. I'm 99% sure it's mould. That's what Google says. It's on the bathroom ceiling too, in the corners. But it's black, green, and white in there. It could be mildew. I don't know the difference. There's a lack of airflow, or too much condensation and moisture in the flat, something like that. Peter doesn't open the blinds or the windows.

Peter's asleep next to me. His snoring is unbearable. He sucks all the air out of the room. If he falls asleep first, I never get to. His sinuses are always blocked, so his mouth is always open. He's dribbling on the pillow. I turn and face the other way. Our digital alarm clock glares at me. It reads 1:07 a.m. The alarm goes off at 7:00 a.m., and we wake to the sounds of BBC Radio Manchester playing the latest hits. Peter likes music in the mornings. He says it helps him prepare for the day. It gives me a headache.

I can hear the constant slow drip of the toilet. There's a slight leak in the cistern somewhere. It makes me need to go. I get out of bed and go to the bathroom. The cold laminate makes my toes feel like ice. I need to buy new slippers. I debate whether to flush the toilet. It's so loud. I decide to. Peter's a heavy sleeper.
I walk back to the bedroom and get back into bed. I'm nodding off when my phone lights up. It's a text from John. He lives in the upstairs flat. He never sleeps either. He asks whether I'm still awake, but he already knows the answer. He's heard the toilet flush. The plumbing is all connected. I don't respond. I'm not going to. I put

the phone on the bedside table and start to settle back down when it lights up again. It's another text from John. He can see I've read the first message and ignored him. He'll only text if he thinks Peter's asleep.

I can feel Peter's hot breath on the back of my neck. It's no use, I can't sleep now. I sit up and swing my legs off the side of our small double bed. There's a glass of water on my bedside table. I take a sip. I don't want to drink too much. I'll need the toilet again and John will know I'm still up. I listen. I can hear the faint rumble of cars on the M60. Through the darkness I can make out the silhouettes of the furniture in our room; two identical oak-effect tables on either side of the bed, a matching chest of drawers, and a half-built flat-pack wardrobe from Argos in a dark mahogany effect. They had run out of the oak when we bought it. Our black roller blind has a tiny hole along the edge on the right. It lets in a thin strip of orange from the streetlight outside.

I look over at Peter, and he hasn't stirred. Peter sleeps naked. He sweats a lot. I'm wearing the red tartan pyjamas he bought me for Christmas. I don't wear underwear with them, and my breasts hang freely underneath. But you wouldn't be able to imagine what my body looked like beneath the fleecy fabric. They're not sexy in the slightest. They're two sizes too big and the shirt buttons right up to the neck. Peter says they're comfy and cosy. He's a practical man. But I'm not interested in comfy and cosy. I want to be seen.

The phone starts to vibrate. John is calling. I quickly end it, slip out of the bed and sneak towards the living room. The floorboards creak in the hall. He calls again.

'Hi there, Jo,' he says.

'What you still doing up?' I speak quietly.

'Oh, ya know me, Jo. Never sleep, do I?' he chuckles and then coughs.

'That baccy too strong for you?' I tease.

'It's only about a quarter of what's making me choke,' he says. 'The bag's right strong this time.' He coughs again. 'So, you coming up?' he asks. 'I've missed ya.'

I grin.

I used to smoke with John most weekends. Peter goes to bed early. He works six days a week. John's wife left him two years ago, and he gets lonely. It makes sense to be friends. But Peter dislikes him; he says he's dodgy. He says he has bad intentions, whatever that means. John's twelve years older than me. But he isn't ageing too badly.

I say, 'Bit late now, isn't it?' I glance at the clock on the wall. It isn't. It's 1:58 a.m.

'Never bothered you before.'

'Peter wouldn't like it,' I tell him.

'Don't tell him then. You didn't last time.'

That was a one-off.

'I'm wearing pyjamas,' I tell John.

'You're only coming upstairs,' John laughs. 'What does that matter?'

'I'm not coming up in *these* pyjamas!' I state.

'Ok. Then get changed. See you in ten,' he says. 'Wait, what colour are they?'

'What? The pyjamas?' I ask.

'Yes.'

'They're red,' I say.

He says, 'You look good in red,' and hangs up.

I creep back to the bedroom and pick up the mid-blue skinny jeans and white V-neck t-shirt I had on yesterday. I wouldn't go round in pyjamas. I open my underwear drawer. I reach for my usuals, then I see the red lingerie set I bought for Christmas. It was for Peter. High-waisted red lace briefs and a sheer-cup underwired bra in the same pillar-box red—they still have the tags on them. Peter said to save them for a special occasion. But I decide there's no point in waiting. I look good in red.

I strip out of the baggy tartan pyjamas, leaving them in a pile on the floor. I'm naked. There's a chill to the air that makes my nipples erect. I shiver. Peter's spread out like a starfish, still snoring. I gather my clothes and go back to the living room to change. I put the lingerie on. I like the feeling of the lace against my skin. I start to feel hot. I used to make an effort for Peter. He used to appreciate it.

I leave the front door on the latch and hold it until it is closed. I slink onto the communal landing and climb the stairs to John's flat.

John is in the doorway, leaning against the frame.

'Ay-up, here she is,' he says. His arms are extended, signalling a hug. I like that he wants to hug me. His eyes are half-open, red and glazed over. We embrace. His breath smells.

'Come on in, sexy,' he shouts. He's forever acting silly.

'Shhh! You're being loud,' I giggle and remind him.

We go inside. I sit on his couch. The room is tidy but dirty. A layer of dust covers the TV unit and coffee table. There are various stains on the cushions. I sit forward in my seat. John goes to the fridge and comes back holding a Carling. There're more empty cans by the foot of his armchair. He sits down and lights another joint. I watch him place it to his lips and inhale. John's only thirty-six, but his weathered complexion and the deep-set lines on his forehead would convince you otherwise. He's not handsome like Peter, but he does make me laugh.

He leans over and passes me the joint. There's dirt in his fingernails. I take a drag and splutter. John's right, it is strong.

'So how is Peter?' John asks.

'Sleeping,' I say.

He doesn't say anything else. He doesn't need to. He's heard it all before. John says Peter should pay more attention to me. He says I need someone who will give me the attention I deserve. John stoops towards me again and takes the joint back. He nods towards my centre. He winks. I glance down. My t-shirt has a red hue across the chest. The white jersey material isn't thick enough to conceal my bra. I shift in my seat. He smirks. I want to tell him to stop fooling around. But I don't. What's the harm in him looking? He's right, someone should. He continues to hold his stare. Peter used to stare like this, with a hunger in his eyes. But he's downstairs, asleep.

I stand up and move to sit on the arm of John's chair. I want to sit closer to him. It makes it easier to smoke. I bend forward, to inhale his blowbacks. He smiles. His teeth are stained yellow, but straight. I bet they would look really good if he started using a little whitening toothpaste, or even brushed them twice a day. I can't imagine he does that. John's hair is still thick. It has no signs of thinning. The sides are greying slightly. I like that. It is slicked back. But not with VO5, or any other gel.

It's slick with grease. I catch a whiff of it in between the smell of the blowbacks. He wouldn't look bad at all if he took better care of himself.

John places a hand on my thigh. I wish it was Peter's hand.

'I'm quite tired now,' I say. I force a yawn. John furrows his brow.

'The fun hasn't even started yet. I've still got another joint for us.'

'I'm knackered,' I say. 'I think I'll go to bed now.' I get up from the arm of the chair. Before John can argue, I leave.

I get back into our flat, lock the door and head for the kitchen. The mints are at the back of the breadbin. I put three in my mouth.

I go to the bedroom. The band of the bra is digging into my sides. The label on the knickers making the bottom of my back itch. I remove my jeans and t-shirt and fling them over the dismantled bits of the wardrobe. I take off the lingerie and fold it up. I put the red lacey set back in its drawer. I put my pyjamas back on. I delete my call history. I delete the texts from John, putting my phone in its place on the bedside table.

Peter's still in the middle of the bed. I push him until he groans and rolls over. There's enough room for me now. I snuggle into Peter's side, comfy and cosy in my red tartan pyjamas. I promise myself that I'll clean the mould in the morning.

Lichen and Lecterns

—— Dorcy Jaffray ——

I HAD DRIVEN PAST THE abandoned church for years. That Thursday, nineteen and desperate, I pulled in. The dirt parking lot crunched angrily under the wheels of my car, berating me for trespassing.

It was hot with no breeze. Beads of sweat dripped down my calves and back. Everything smelled green. The church was tucked into the woods, covered with vines as if it had grown with the trees. Saplings into towering trunks. Bricks into thick walls and a crooked cross.

I didn't try the front door. God might notice me. Instead, I inched around the back, following a haphazard trail of rotting planks. I stepped on the toes of my sneakers, worried about disturbing something I was afraid didn't exist.

The path opened to reveal descending seats made of stone. Moss was draped everywhere, crawling toward the church. This was natural, untainted by prayer books and bibles. A space of worship enclosed by ageing oaks and neglect. My best chance.

Nudging aside damp leaves and broken sticks, I settled in the middle. I hugged my knees, trying to make myself as small as possible. I wanted to feel something. Anything.

In front of me sat a lectern tilting to one side. I stared at the rocks and waited. *I'm here now.* I had slipped past the barrier. Snuck into something sacred. I waited to be spit out. But there was nothing.

I approached the lectern, pulling out a cheap cigarette and tucking it between my teeth. Lichen twisted and curled around the edges of the stone. I traced the pattern with one finger, watching the velvet algae bend beneath my touch. Gazing out at my invisible congregation, I blew out a stream of smoke and began my sermon.

A Stitch of God

—*Hayli McClain*—

IT'S NOT THAT YOU'VE ALWAYS dreamed of crocheting a wooly off-white scarf. It's that your great-aunt Beatrice is killer good at crochet, and she used to make you something every Christmas, and you hate to imagine this dying with her.

She introduced the scarf as 'the easiest darn thing in the world'. Double crochet over and over—all you've gotta do is count. You can count, can't you? Twenty-eight years old, she *hopes* you can count to fifteen, turn the scarf, count to fifteen again. Sure, but you didn't expect to struggle so bad with yarn over, yarn under, yarn where-exactly? Your progress is slower-going than Auntie Bea's. She's cradled, porcelain-frail, in her armchair. You hunch cross-legged beside her slippers.

'Oh, whoops.' You did something wrong a few rows back. You spot it, now: a wonky gap where there should've been a stitch but isn't. Guess you can't count after all. You hold the error up for Auntie Bea's inspection. 'Should I pull it out and fix that?'

'No.' Auntie Bea swats the idea away with a veiny hand. 'That stitch belongs to God, is all.'

You're not sure you believe in God. You definitely don't know why He or She or They would want your scarf to have a pokey hole in it.

'Only God is perfect,' Auntie Bea explains. 'If you don't make a mistake by mistake, leave a little one on purpose. Nothin' to notice, except by God, who'll look kindly on your humility.'

You leave the mistake where it is, and suddenly you can't shake the feeling that your soul is shot through with humble stitches; bunch of mess-ups and holes big enough to tangle your hand in. You'll try not to mess up anymore. You'll try to get it right.

Auntie Bea finishes her own scarf. She scissors its umbilical connection to the skein, then makes the tail of it vanish. She asks, 'D'you want this, sweetie?' and you say, 'Yes, please,' because twenty-eight's not too grown for aw-thanks-my-aunt-made-it-for-me. You search for a glimpse of God in her handiwork, but it's too humbly hidden. You continue with your own scarf, wearing its far-superior twin around your neck.

Auntie Bea gives a content sigh. She pulls a half-length afghan-in-progress onto her lap. Sale yarn, still orange-stickered, but soft. Robin's-egg blue. She likes using bright colors, to cheer the hearts of those who need it. She switches crochet hooks and picks up where she'd left off.

'I usually say my prayers while I work,' Auntie Bea tells you. 'D'you mind?'

Of course, you don't. This is the last-chance extra closeness you came here for.

'Alrighty.' Auntie Bea draws a not-very-deep breath; best she can manage. 'Lord, thank you for today. Thank you for the fact that I got myself an eager student.' She pats you on the head. It warms you with such sloshing-bright pride that you feel baby-teeth young and want to labor on this poor excuse of a scarf forever under Auntie Bea's eyes. 'And thank you for keepin' my hands useful. Thank you also for the pretty snowflakes outside. Chunky fellas. You make such pretty things, Lord.'

Her fingers work yarn over, yarn through, yarn over, yarn through. The Biblical violence of God isn't for you. But, you think, as your old auntie's tissue-thin voice gently rosary-rubs prayer into every stitch of a heaven-blue afghan, that you'd love to give God's mercy a try.

'Lord, I pray for those who are cold,' Auntie Bea murmurs. 'That You would make them warm.'

Six to eight months, the doctor said seven months ago. Auntie Bea doesn't eat much. Doesn't sleep much. But she can still bust out an afghan start to finish between a Friday and a Monday. This boggles your mind. It makes you want to cry over the words of an obituary not yet written. *Has anyone kept count?* you wonder.

Does anyone know how many dozens/hundreds/thousands of scarves and hats and blankets Auntie Bea's donated in her life?

She notices that you've stopped crocheting. She raises her brows, staring at you with eyes magnified behind ultra-thick glasses.

'God wants *active* hands in prayer,' Auntie Bea says. 'You remember that.'

You will.

You'll remember it all your life.

Rambling in the Time of Covid

—— *Ruth Irons* ——

IF IT WEREN'T FOR THE Saltire and Jolly Roger flapping and snapping in the prevailing south-westerly wind, you'd probably drive straight past our house without even noticing it. Even the road signs relegate the row of four post-war semis to a no-man's land beyond the bounds of a hamlet with no shop, no church, nothing but a slightly scruffy pub. But for most of 2020 this former farmworker's cottage was the axis around which my whole world revolved. Coronavirus shrunk the frontiers of our lives. It confined us to home, cut us off from family and friends, denied us all but the most essential car journeys – to the supermarket, mostly, to queue up for rare luxuries such as toilet roll and pasta – and forced us to sterilise our social and professional interactions through the filter of a screen.

Look out of any window in our house and you'll see farmland, trees, hills, and lots of sky. We're surrounded by fields on three sides and a dense patch of woodland on the fourth. A glimpse of Arcadia in north-east Fife. Yet, since Rosie, our Cairn terrier, died almost eight years ago, I had rarely gone for a walk just for the sheer joy of it. There's something about a dog which legitimises an amble through the woods or a stroll along the beach, stopping here and there to take in the view under the guise of scooping poop. Without a canine companion, I'd feel self-conscious, slightly suspect. But the pandemic—and the First Minister—gave me permission to take daily exercise, dogless and fancy free, for my physical and mental health. So, I downloaded Strava on my phone, fished out my walking boots from the back of the cupboard, and locked the front door behind me.

Before lockdown, my only reason for walking south from our house and venturing over the offset crossroads would be to drop an occasional letter or card into the post box in the wall of the pub. Now, I carried on along the narrow pavement and past the handful of squat bungalows which marked the start of an ancient coffin road. I stopped briefly to put in my headphones, walked between two redundant stone gateposts, and set off up the hill.

For the first few hundred yards the lane was well maintained, but it quickly became rutted and pockmarked. It was soon more potholes than track, and I weaved from side to side with the unsteady gait of a drunk staggering home after too many pints and a whisky chaser, attempting to avoid the pools of muddy, rainbow-slicked water. Specks of grit inveigled their way through the holes in my tatty boots, niggling and nipping like the irksome pea in Hans Christian Andersen's tale. I wobbled on my left leg as I gave my right boot a vigorous shake, and then reversed the process, touching my socked toes briefly on the crumbling tarmac for balance. The relief was short-lived; within three or four paces new stones had taken their place.

Patches of weeds poked through the loose chippings, their yellow flowers and white seed heads widening the fissures in the surface. They looked like miniature dandelions, but my knowledge of flora and fauna is sketchy at best, and I took a photo on my phone so I could look them up later. Whatever they were, there was something heroic in the way these insignificant-looking plants, each stem and leaf and petal easily crushed underfoot or between thumb and forefinger, could displace tar and rubble with their dogged thrusting towards the light.

To my right the land dipped steeply beyond a low stone wall, flattening into an expanse of arable farmland, some lying winter-fallow, the rest planted with a cereal crop in neat green rows. Our quartet of cottages faced me from across a further stubbled field, smoke curling from the chimney of my house at the far end. It was just half a kilometre away as the crow flies, but several times that via the road, thanks to the railway line which bisected the landscape.

The ascent was growing steeper, and I was unfit. I spurred myself onwards with breathless mutterings. *Just twenty more steps. Keep going until the next tree. You can stop at that gateway.* A small herd of brown and black cattle clustered around two loose haystacks in the corner of a meadow where the track gave way to a metalled road. The animals jostled for the sweetest clumps, stalks falling from their mouths to augment the thick, soft layer of bedding which covered the ground. A few calves—no longer cute newborns, more likely bovine teenagers, judging by their baleful stares—watched as I leaned on the fence for a couple of minutes to recover, and then zigzagged round the edge of the pasture and on up the hill.

The lane gave way at the top to a trail strewn with dry needles and cones from the spindly firs which populated the northern slope, looming over the sturdy ash trees opposite. A shallow burn flowed down a narrow gully, bearing flotsam from the trees and the forest floor which wedged in places to form makeshift dams. Gnarled roots stretched across the path like varicose veins, contorting between knobbles of bedrock in a tacit pact to trip the unwary hiker.

I gradually became aware of a rhythmic thrumming: slow, measured, mechanical, rising in a steady crescendo. As I stepped out from the woods into a huge, open field, it receded, almost obliterated by the noise of the blustering wind which battered through my thin fleece and buffeted my eardrums. A wind turbine stretched skywards from among the barley, its three blades turning in nonchalant pirouettes. To the north, Dundee nestled against the backdrop of the Sidlaws, centuries of history emerging through the haze. Mediaeval church towers huddled alongside nineteenth-century mill stacks and a few surviving multis from the 1960s; social and architectural aberrations, which had so far evaded the fate of their peers, demolished in a cloud of dust and debris during the past decade. The war memorial and radio mast on the summit of the Law overlooked three colossal red and white oil rigs, like giant Meccano, towed hundreds of miles to the Tay from their footings in the North Sea to be repaired or dismantled.

From up here, less than ten kilometres away and only a hundred or so metres above sea level, Scotland's fourth largest city looked like a model village. Half a millennium of industry dwarfed by an extinct volcano and a cordon of undulating hills. Nature putting human constructs firmly in their place. I hadn't needed to walk far or climb high to gain a new perspective on the familiar.

The heavy, rusty spring screeched against its steel shank as I wrenched open the gate into the woods. The harsh sound was answered almost immediately by the glottal, rattling cry of two male pheasants, flushed out of the bracken by my noisy arrival. Despite the warmth and brightness of the day, the rugged path between the Scots pines was cool and shaded. Occasional blinding flashes of sunlight between the upper branches cast a fleeting spotlight on clusters of bright yellow daffodils and the vivid green moss which carpeted the woodland floor.

I followed the narrow trail as it jinked and twisted between tree roots and rabbit holes. Ducking and stumbling to avoid the jagged thorns of gorse and bramble, I soon reached a broader track, furnished with a slalom of obstacles cobbled together from tree trunks, old tyres, and railway sleepers. A riding club sign was painted on the first jump in large, shaky white letters. I'd never seen anyone taking their horse over this course, although the hoof prints in the soft earth and the generous mounds of fresh manure told a different story.

Two tufts of white hair bobbing through the undergrowth caught my attention. Roe deer. Signs of their presence are everywhere; branches and trunks stripped of their bark, a lattice of narrow paths through the vegetation, even the ticks which the cats unwittingly bring home from their nocturnal forays. I'd occasionally spotted deer before, but always much earlier in the morning, late at night, or, too often, as bloated carcasses at the side of the road after a final, ill-judged leap into oblivion. Now, seduced by the relative absence of traffic and human predators to graze in the middle of the day, they sprang between the bushes, among the trees, managing somehow to combine grace and panic in a single, fluid movement. Before I could get my phone out of my pocket to capture the moment, they were gone.

I passed a series of blue pheasant feeder barrels and hopped over the trodden-down remains of a wire fence into open fields. A sparse strip of gorse and broom bushes straggled across the land like diminutive waymarkers. Young winter wheat lay to one side; on the other was untilled ground, the bare earth baked hard like clay, with jagged cracks splitting the surface and tussocks of coarse grass shouldering their way through the arid soil.

Ahead of me a little-used bridleway stretched from left to right, with telegraph poles set at regular intervals along its edge. The old railway line. I couldn't blame Dr Beeching for this one. It closed almost a decade before his brutal amputations. A deep drainage ditch ran parallel with the low embankment, the stagnant water covered in the delicate creamy blooms of a pond weed, roots anchored in the mud and petals drifting on the brackish water like confetti. Painted Lady butterflies, their wings splattered with white, black, and amber splodges, fluttered and flitted between the flowers, unperturbed by my scrutiny.

I felt a few spots of rain on my face, and being an unashamedly fair-weather walker, I retreated to the shelter of the woods via a colonnade of beech trees. They rose from a spongy blanket of furred husks from last year's nut harvest, discarded by the red squirrels which had long since pillaged and hoarded the sweet kernels. Badgers had dug their setts in among the shallow roots, scrabbling out heaps of sandy soil to create low, domed openings. Hidden away in every corner of forest and farmland were the secret sanctuaries of woodland creatures. I must have tramped past and over and through their homes a hundred times without even realising. Now, as an insistent drizzle spilled from the darkening sky, it was time to return to mine.

I pushed aside the brambles and squeezed out through a narrow gap in the hedge, past the pastel-painted hives from which our worker bees were emerging as the light and warmth of the morning sun hit the narrow entrances. Stepping over the waterlogged craters gouged out by heavy farm vehicles, I set off across the field.

The lower section was covered with rows of stubble, which crackled and crunched in time with my footsteps as I traipsed up the slope. Flocks of small, streaked brown birds took flight from their nests concealed among the stalks, piping in shrill protest at my incursion. Meadow pipits, according to the pocket guide tucked into my backpack. Without it, I can recognise a mere handful of bird species, and then only the obvious ones like robins, blackbirds, and herons. That's about my limit. The childhood trips designed to encourage my brother David's interest in birdwatching bred sullen, bored resentment in me and Simon, the eldest. The two of us shuffled through RSPB reserves with the reluctance of Shakespeare's whining schoolboy, and slouched in the corners of hushed, darkened hides with adolescent apathy seeping from every pore. Now I was surprised by my own delight as I stood and watched the pipits soaring and swooping in ever-shifting swirls above my head. How much had I missed out on during the intervening half-century? As Kathleen Jamie writes,

'This, after only an hour of attention. What would a year be like, a lifetime, a thousand years? How attuned a person, a whole people, could become.' I have a lot of catching up to do.

The fallow ground gave way to an early sowing of carrots, their frilled leaves poking a few inches through the crumbly grey earth. I picked my way along the chevron tractor tracks which formed pathways between the crops, careful not to trample any of the young plants. I stopped on the crest of the hill to catch my breath and looked back towards the house. The blue sky was smeared with wisps of cirrus cloud like daubs from an artist's brush, and a murder of crows circled their rookery high up in the pines in the far corner of the field, calling to one another with rasping caws. A solitary buzzard strayed into their airspace, and immediately a trio of the smaller birds swerved to repel it, mobbing and harassing it with pugnacious cries. Besieged and outnumbered, the buzzard fled.

Up ahead, a row of houses stood along the fringe of the farm, overlooking the fairways and flagsticks of the local golf club. I'm not a fan of golf courses. They disfigure the landscape, their bunkers pitting the countryside like chicken pox scars. But here was a far more pleasing scene. A small lake, fringed with rushes, lay in a hollow, with gentle ripples moving across the water at the nudge of a light breeze. Around it, the grass was mown in precise, contrasting stripes, even in lockdown. Acres of arching polytunnels shimmered in the distance like the swell of waves in a placid ocean. It would be churlish of me to nurse my disapproval in such a tranquil setting.

I wandered across the deserted greens, past the clubhouse and along the side of the driving range. Beyond a few token strands of fence wire was a steep incline, covered in brown, desiccated bracken and vicious nettles. The contrast was stark, as though nature were aggressively reasserting herself in defiance of the golf course's manicured perfection. At the top stood an unkempt thicket of silver birch trees, their limbs infested with pustules of dusty orange mould. Scrambling between the low boughs and under the drooping branches of an adjacent larch grove, I was startled by a strange cacophony—snuffles, snorts, and squeals, overlaid with the raucous cackles of scavenging gulls. Aluminium pig arks littered the rough plateau on the brow of the hill, shelter for the sows which wandered through the trotter-churned mud, tiny piglets tottering in their wake, or suckled their offspring from udders distended with milk.

An aged oak, its elephantine trunk more than five feet across, stood sentinel over the boundary between the pig farm and the cemetery. Clambering down through a tangle of ferns and brambles, I steadied myself on the dry-stone wall which hugged the perimeter, dislodging a couple of loose chunks of grey sandstone in the process. It must be very satisfying to create these three-dimensional jigsaws—the nearest I have come is stacking the logs for our wood-burning stove—and a drystane dyking course is on my bucket list. A narrow, gravelled footpath curved around to the entrance of the graveyard, which is terraced in broad layers and crowned by an ornate chapel, its steep copper roof weathered to a dull green finish.

I dropped by for a quick chat with half a dozen friends, nearly all taken from us far too soon. Their graves are tended with love and adorned with candles and fresh flowers. But there was another resting place, obscure and little-known, which I wanted to visit. Norman, a six-year-old boy lost to diphtheria in 1898, is buried on a precipitous, overgrown bank which drops down behind the cemetery. It's always saddened me to see this child's solitary grave, separated for eternity from the engineers, lawyers, soldiers and ministers of the parish by a neatly clipped yew hedge. Yet since I was last here, someone had placed a toy van and fishing boat and a bunch of orange silk roses on the narrow plinth of the small stone cross which marks the wee lad's living and dying. I wish I'd thought of it. But I'm glad someone did. I silently thanked Norman's unknown benefactor and turned for home.

Since I began my ramblings, lockdown has eased and we have started to move slowly—but far from surely—back to something that passes for normal. The roads are jammed with cars again, commuters and tourists fill the trains which run between Edinburgh and Aberdeen on the railway line just across the field, and the sky is criss-crossed once more with the impromptu Saltires of intersecting vapour trails from military jets and holiday flights.

But as familiar patterns emerged in the fabric of our lives, nature staged a swift and brutal intervention. Storm Arwen felled and fractured millions of trees across Scotland. She reshaped the landscape, destroyed the homes of countless animals which dwell, seen or unseen, in our woodland, and the routes by which they—and we—traverse it. New paths are already appearing, trodden by cervine hooves or hacked by human tools. And I will follow them, as I keep walking, exploring, **discovering**. Taking time, as William Henry Davies exhorts us, to stand and stare. My life will surely be all the richer for it.

The Morning of the Family Funeral

——Morgan Carmichael——

MAUDE'S BEEN IN THE SHOWER for twenty-five minutes.

I'm giving her another five and then I'm gonna go check she hasn't killed herself.

I'm sitting on the bed and waiting for some kind of human noise to occur inside the bathroom.

A shifting of her feet.

A suppression of crying.

But there's no life anywhere inside the house.

So, I fixate myself on the bathroom door from my bed; it's always fascinated me because it's so weird looking. Right in the middle of the door, all the painting is chipping off in vertical strokes. If I forget about it for a few days, then look at it again, it always seems to grow, as though someone was sneaking into my house and stripping off small bits of wood at a time.

Sometimes, when the lights are off in the hallway, the cracks look like a melted face. It makes me feel grossed out and lonely.

Maude's Grandpa Bill's funeral is in two hours. I'm dressed for the funeral, waiting on her. Always, always waiting on Maude.

To get dressed.

To finish eating.

To grow.

To be happy.

As my mum used to say, 'To work slowly isn't to work humanly.' Mum was a bright woman, as though she had days where she could forget that the fibre of everyone's being was meaningless.

The chauvinistic smell of blue Radox is sweating into the bedroom now, making its way through the house like a bad mood. Maude's taken to using it since her grandpa died because it's what he used. She puts too much on and comes to bed smelling of it. Some nights I wake up and forget where I am, as though I were in love with men again.

Grandpa Bill used a lot of it too; every fortnight he would buy a new bottle. It wasn't even like he had a lot of money, he was just careless with it. I'd try to talk to Maude about his expenditure and she'd just say; 'You're too rational, it's no fun.'

Maude and her grandfather were very close. She lived with him in her early teens, when she realised she hated her parents. For the first two months of our relationship, I thought they were dead.

Sometimes, Maude still seems like a kid, just in ageing skin.

This is Maude's first close, familial death, and she's mimicking her grandfather just like she has whenever famous people die. It's as though Maude can't deal with them not being there anymore, so she just becomes them. It's her own sick way of coping with grief; like when Bowie died, she painted a big fuck off zigzag on her face. She wants the whole world to look at her and grieve too.

I'm fed up now and concerned. I stand up and walk across the hall, to the bathroom door. As I approach the door, she opens it and her body jerks slightly in fright. She has white towels wrapped around her body and head; she's all white with occasional flesh.

She looks up at me. 'Why're you always hovering?'

'I was just coming to check you were alright.'

Maude's confused face and disgusted face look the same. 'Why wouldn't I be alright?'

I shrug.

She walks around me to go into the bedroom. I follow her to the room and just stand in the doorway. She picks socks from the drawer and then puts them on the bed, trying to decide on a pair. She's passing time by being an idiot.

Maude and I don't live together, she just has a drawer of stuff at my place. Since her grandpa passed, she's been here all the time, just being mean or in bed, but death will always help you grow into a worse version of yourself.

'You want a hand getting ready?' I ask, bored of watching her try to keep busy.

'My grandpa's died, not my ability to move.' She doesn't look at me as she talks. It's moments like this that I want to leave her. I'm set off yet drawn in by the smallest of things.

'And besides,' she continues, 'no man ought to have any say on how a woman presents herself. That's why the world is always at war: too many men in charge and too many women defenceless for it. I mean, look at Afghanistan.' She decides on a baby pink pair of socks and puts them on.

'What does me helping you pick out socks have to do with Afghanistan?... You make everything so ... political,' I say, shaking my head slightly. I hate political people, outwardly because they're loud and arrogant and cocky, and secretly because they make me feel insecure and stupid. 'I mean, picking out socks isn't a commentary on gender roles.'

'Everything's political, Henry...' she says, fixing her last sock at the heel. She stands up straight, puts her face in her hands, then goes back to looking normal and I watch all her movements and wonder what'll come out of her mouth next. 'I'm sorry...' she says suddenly, 'that was dick-ish of me.' She comes up and takes my hands in hers.

'Don't you think that saying is funny? As though having a dick makes you automatically an arsehole?'

She gives a small, unconvincing laugh through her nose, but her grandpa is dead after all.

'So, what are you going to wear?' I ask.

'I don't know... I'm between the dress or the trousers and blouse.' She points to the items as she says them. I prefer the dress, but perhaps that makes me seem a misogynist, even though I don't mean to be. If I were, my mum would find a way to skelp my arse from the ground. She was pro everything that wasn't wrong, pro-LGBTQ, pro-human rights, pro-choice, pro-environment. Sometimes when I feel like I'm forgetting her I donate to random pro so-and-so charities.

Maude walks over to the clothes like there are weights on her hips. 'I just think it's crazy,' she adds.

'What is?'

'Getting dressed to watch someone go into the ground … Remember when we got the call to say he was dying?'

I nod.

'Well, we had to get dressed to go to the hospital and that's so weird to me; having to put on clothes to watch someone die,' she starts to shake her head, as though she can't believe how wise she sounds.

'Yeah … you're right, I've never thought of that before.'

'See the other day? I ate an apple and accidentally ate some of the seeds, do you think that the apple or flowers will grow inside me and kill me?'

I laugh, then realise she's serious.

'No, Maude, that's not possible. People swallow seeds accidentally all the time and they're fine.'

Maude seems to think that death runs in the family, like a cold; one gets it, then you all get it.

'Don't you think that would be a beautiful way to go? Suffocated in flowers.'

'Yeah,' I say. 'It would.'

She puts on her dress and I feel the urge to tell her I'm here for her, but sometimes 'my nice-ness stresses her out', so I just smile when she shows me how she looks, and she seems content with my expression. I can't help but notice how tired she looks. She hasn't slept properly since her grandpa's passing. For a week after, she kept seeing his face when she fell asleep, and she started to grow afraid that she would wake up and find him at the end of the bed.

'Do you want a cup of tea? Before we leave?' I ask.

'Please, that would be nice.' She's sitting at the desk struggling to get the clasp of her necklace.

'Here, I'll do it.'

'Thanks,' she says in an out-breath, as though she's relieved someone cares about her.

I get her necklace on. 'I like that necklace, it goes really well.'

She smiles tiredly then holds onto my hand that's drooped on her shoulder for a moment. I smile back and leave the room, leaving behind her hand and damaged spirit.

I go into the kitchen and get two black mugs out. It was Maude who taught me how to make a good cup of tea. When she caught me putting the milk in first, she called it British blasphemy.

Teabag,

Water in,

Stir, stir, pinch teabag into the side of the mug, stir again,

Teabag out,

Milk in,

Two sugars,

Stir.

I boil the kettle and put the tea bags in. I hate seeing Maude without power, it feels worse than her being sad. I want to crawl inside her head and change her mind.

'Oh, fucking hell,' Maude says, walking into the loose wood beams as she enters the kitchen. She then walks around the frame, dodging it even though she's a mile away from it.

'It's not going to grow legs, Maude,' I say, handing her her tea.

I'm getting work done on the kitchen and it's a fucking mess; it's all loose wood beams and the fridge is on slants, so it shakes every time you open or close the door, as though it's trying to run away. I somehow manage to forget that almost every day as though this weren't my life, and I weren't living in it.

'I don't understand why you're re-doing the kitchen, what's the point if you won't be here forever? Like, you'll die, we'll all die, so what's the point in doing up kitchens or anything?' She leans back on the counter, visibly tired from her own spiralling.

I take another sip of tea. 'But that's just how life works. I mean, we all die, you can't not live life just because one day you won't anymore … death is natural.'

'Naturality *cannot* be enough to comfort people, surely!'

I shrug again.

'Death doesn't scare you?'

119

I shake my head slightly. 'Not really.'

'You're crazy, man.'

The radio is still on from when I put it on earlier this morning. It's currently playing *Attractive Female Wanted* by Rod Stewart. Prick.

'God, don't you wish you could skip a song on the radio,' I say.

Maude stays motionless. It makes me feel lonely.

'We should probably finish getting ready so we aren't late, no?' I say.

There's a silence for a few seconds.

'Why do good people die? Like, why do the good get shit and the shit get good?' She stands with her arms down by her sides like a protection stance, as though trying to guard herself from the fact people around her are dying.

'Maude, your grandpa was like … eighty something … it was natural for him to go. It's not about being good or bad sometimes.'

'But he could have had like another ten years…' Her eyes fill as she says that, though she hasn't cried yet. It's as though moths are entering into her ears and eating her emotions.

'You can't think about it that way … you'll make yourself sick with your own thoughts.' I'm getting sick of the questions she keeps asking me; every question makes me feel more and more useless. Some days I just feel like a piece of dust under the bed.

'Maybe I should try to put some music out there. You know I always wanted to do that; I write good stuff, you said that yourself.'

When Bowie died, she developed an obsession with becoming known and famous. As though status makes your death more meaningful. Perhaps it does. She wants to die in a way that the whole world grieves her, wants the whole world to look at her and feel something, as though everyone ought to be in love with her.

'Yeah, you could if you wanted to.'

I turn around and put my mug into the sink.

'I think I'm gonna change. I don't want to feel so girly today. It doesn't seem appropriate,' she says, suddenly. 'I'll be quick,' she says, grabbing my hand. It feels as though she's begging, and it makes me feel predatorial.

I decide not to have a temper. 'Okay, babe. I'll be in the living room and let you finish getting ready.'

I go into the living room and sit on the couch and think about how I want this to be over. Goodbyes are the worst thing in the world, even if it's for someone you don't know that well. Is it a selfish thing, to apply yourself to someone else's grief? I'm not sure grief can be that straightforward.

I want a whisky. I go into the kitchen whilst Maude is getting ready and get a glass and slide the bottle from the wall towards me. I start to pour.

'Henry!' she shouts from the bedroom.

'Yeah!'

We often find ourselves communicating through shouts; through different rooms; communicating without looking at each other in the face. We used to find it funny.

'Are you drinking?'

'Yeah!'

'...Pour me one, will you?' she shouts back.

I get out another glass and debate whether I should give her a small measure or a big one. I don't want her to feel tipsy for the funeral, but I also don't want her to feel as weighted as she does now. I decide to go for a small measure, in the name of sensibility and so forth.

I bring her the glass and she tans the whole thing in one impressive gulp, then sets the glass down on the desk beside her. I sip mine slowly as she finishes getting dressed.

'Will you do this button at the back of the blouse, I can't reach it.'

I do it for her. I find my current dread a funny thing because Maude and I are probably immersed in the same feelings at this moment. It's almost romantic.

I gulp the rest of my drink and put my wallet in my pocket. I want to buy her family some drinks during the reception. I plan out my kindness so much I wonder if it's kindness at all. Perhaps kindness is only so if it's spontaneous.

'I can't do this,' she says suddenly, her body in a slouch, as though her grief were pushing her to the floor.

'Yes, you can ... It'll be over before you know it, I promise.'

I want to tell her that she can't reverse this, because a lack of control can be the most soothing thing in the world at times.

'The funeral, yeah, but the death won't. It won't ever go away, it's irreversible. The funeral is just a sick prelude.'

I get the feeling that Maude isn't so much sad about the death as about her own life, mourning her own future, and what's to come, rather than her grandpa's demise.

'I can't do this, Henry, I can't do it,' she goes and stands in the corner of the room as though she's scared of being hit. I feel like a nasty father, suddenly. 'I can't deal with knowing he's spending the rest of my life in a box.'

The image of my mum in a box comes to mind. It makes me want to puke.

'He was the only grandfather I ever had.'

Maude's dad didn't speak to his father, only her mother spoke to hers.

I have nothing to say, so I stay silent with the rest of the room. Then, I suddenly remember what my mum said to me when she was dying.

'Maude … will you do something for me?'

'What?' She says, tiredly.

'Will you look out the window for me?'

She gives me that confused, disgusted look again.

I repeat myself and she eventually does it. I stand behind her.

'Okay … you see how those clouds are moving?'

She nods, though her stance indicates she's not interested.

'Well, that's life. It's always moving and that's a beautiful thing. If life didn't move, your grandfather wouldn't have … fallen in love, or retired, or grown old, he wouldn't be here at all if those clouds didn't move just like they are now. It was those clouds, that made you have a grandpa at all. Life moving isn't scary, it's natural … and the world won't stop just because he's gone even if you think it might.'

She just sniffs.

'You wanna hear something funny? When I was a kid, I used to think that the clouds were being moved by all the spirits and dead people, that they were up there moving life for the rest of us. Sometimes, I was even scared they did it so that they could have us back with them quicker.'

'I like that thought; moving and living so that we get closer to seeing them.'

It was a pretty depressing way for her to live her life, but if it made her feel better, she could have it.

She wipes her eyes and lets out a sigh. 'Right … I'll go re-do my mascara quickly.'

'Okay.'

She walks to the bathroom and stops short at the door. I feel panicked for a moment that we're going to go backwards again, but instead, she turns back to me and opens her mouth. 'Have you ever noticed that there's a face in the door?'

'You see the face?' I ask, surprised.

'Yeah … it looks weird.'

'Oh, well this is quite awkward cause I actually thought it looked like you?'

'It does not!' she says, though she makes a face that shows she's holding back laughter. It makes her look pretend, it's adorable. She goes into the bathroom and gets the mascara. She puts some on the bit of the melted face that looks like eyes.

'Now it looks like me,' she says.

'A masterpiece!'

She laughs and I do too. A beautiful sound let loose into the air for us to share. Then, she laughs until she starts to cry and the way the wood on the door looks, makes the face look like it's crying too and suddenly, I want to caress them both, forever.

Isolation Again!

——*Liza Miles*——

POLLY REACHED HER ARM FROM under the duvet to shut down the alarm. Cat had been telling her it was time to rise and shine for quite a while already, nuzzling and trying to paw her way under the covers. But Polly Brisbane wasn't in the mood to get out of bed anytime soon.

'God, another day of isolation,' she said aloud. Cat's paw took a swipe at her nose. 'Ouch, claws, Caterina,' annunciating the feline's name in full as a reprimand. 'Why did I have to get Covid now, just as everything's opening up again?'

'*Well Polly, if you hadn't insisted on popping up to the wine bar last weekend, maybe you wouldn't have. Choices, choices.*' The critical voice of her long dead presbyterian grandmother, which Polly called Speech Bubble, was already wide awake. During the long lockdowns these internal conversations had sometimes been comforting, a change from talking to Cat, but this morning the critical voice rankled. Who needed a lecture on consequences before the sun was up?

'Meeeoooowwwww.' Cat's patience was running low.

'Alright, alright, the both of you,' grumbled Polly as she fished her slippers from under the bed. Following Cat's eager gambolling, she shuffled through to the kitchen and was confronted by a sink full of unwashed dishes.

'*Polly Brisbane, that's absolutely disgusting.*' Speech Bubble screeched.

'I'm allowed to be a slob sometimes, surely. I'm sick for God's sake.' Polly sniffed, as she emptied the bowl of cold water out and looked forlornly at the pile of plates which hadn't washed themselves.

'*Slob? I can think of another word for it,*' snipped back Speech Bubble. '*No wonder you're still living alone.*'

'I like living alone,' Polly said as she ran hot water and poured liquid soap over the dishes. She caught her reflection in the window of the kitchen. She was changed. She no longer coloured her hair, there were definite new lines in the skin of her round face and the recent 'do it yourself' trim from waist-length to shoulder length was not quite even. Where had the past four years gone? She had been sixty when she made the decision to leave Canada and return to her maternal family's home of Scotland. Three years had passed since she thought about the possibility of an intimate relationship. A dating disaster, the year after she arrived in Scotland, had led her to conclude that sex was more trouble than it was worth. Which was fortunate given a year later the world was swept up in a pandemic.

With the kitchen cleaned to the satisfaction of 'everyone', Polly made a large cup of tea in her favourite mug, decorated with cats, her daughter had sent for her birthday. She switched on the radio for the 7.30 news and spat out the mouthful of tea, belly laughing. The announcer had reported more Partygate shenanigans at "Drowning Street", before correcting himself.

'What do you think, Cat? We've all done isolation time, more time than if I'd robbed a flaming bank. Yet down South, that lot have been breaking the rules and getting it on with Moet and Chandon. And what does that numpty mean he didn't realise he was at a party ... as if!' Polly turned the dial to a local music station.

'*That you done Polly? Had your say?*' Speech Bubble piped up.

'No need for sarcasm. It just feels wrong, doesn't it, Cat? One rule for them and one for us. George Orwell had it right,' Polly said, nuzzling the short haired black feline who was purring, tucked in next to her on the sofa. 'Day seven of isolation, what shall we do?'

'*You might want to shower and get out of those PJs for a change. If you're not careful, you'll be nipping out to Tesco in them next week,*' said Speech Bubble.

Polly ignored the inner voice and carried on talking to Cat, who had just let out an appreciative meow. 'You're right, Cat. It's Jay's birthday. We can call the birthday girl later on. I suppose I had better take a shower and put on clean PJs. Even

125

I can tell I'm a bit whiffy. Then we'll have to find something to do. Lucky you, never having to change your bib and tucker, and you have a portable paw shower.'

'Yes, for goodness' sakes get moving, if you spend another entire day on the couch, you'll seize up altogether. Sixties are the new fifties, or hadn't you heard? But PJs, again really?'

'Oh, the voice of my nemesis. Alright, stop nagging, I KNOW!'

Polly usually sang in the shower; she didn't have a fan in the bathroom and wondered if her neighbour or anyone passing by could hear her through the open window. Not that it bothered her much if they could. Today, she proclaimed vigorously, she was gonna wash that man right out of her hair.

She had just wrapped herself in a light blue fluffy bath sheet when she heard the Skype call start up on her computer. She had forgotten she'd arranged a call with her boss at 8.30.

'Yikes, it's already that time?' Polly hunted for the piece of printed 'my choice' tape she had been sent after she had attended an internet safety course. The facilitator had advised the group to attach the tape over any computer camera to avoid internet peeping toms spying on them.

'Told you to get dressed earlier.'

Flustered by her lack of clothes, Polly turned down the music and accepted the call. 'Hi, Michael.'

'I can't see you. Is there something wrong with your camera, Polly?'

'Sorry, it's the tape …'

'You're fixing it with tape? Are you prepared for the meeting on Monday? I have some more ideas you could work on. How many more days to go in isolation?'

'Yes, Polly, are you prepared?' Speech Bubble chimed in. *'Having spent yesterday staring out of the window instead of at the presentation you were supposed to be working on.'*

'I needed a break, now shut up.'

'Sorry Polly, I didn't quite catch that, my little one started screaming.'

'I said three, and I needed to make a folder up.'

'Ha-ha, for a minute there, Polly, I thought you told me to shut up.'

'Nice one, Polly,' said Speech Bubble.

'Oh heavens, really? Sorry, the line is not very clear.'

'We're now meeting with Nathan at ten on Monday. I hope it'll go well, it's a big deal for us. Please make sure you figure out your camera. Tape's probably not gonna work too well. I can order you another detachable if that one's bust. Just ping me a request.

'We're meeting with Nathan. How come it's not the lycra-wearing dragon?'

'Polly!'

'Ooops, sorry. But I didn't make up the nickname, you did.'

'Did I? Not the point, walls and cameras and tech have ears, Polly. Remember from the training? Try and be careful.'

'I'm sorry. I promise I'll be prepared and well-behaved on Monday. See you then.' Polly clicked end call before Michael could say anything else. She didn't have it in her to take on any more of his ideas for the presentation she was supposed to be organising.

'Polly Brisbane, why are you flushed? The man couldn't see you were only wearing a towel.'

Polly put her hands up to her face. Why was she flushed? She hadn't spoken to Nathan since before the pandemic, when he'd bought her a coffee after the conference and Michael had made a comment to 'be careful with him.' Had she imagined he was flirting with her? Nathan was a bit of a silver fox who probably treated all the women he met or worked with like that. She circled 10am Monday into her daybook and groaned.

'10am is hardly first thing, Polly, you'll just have to get back into routine and stop hanging out with Cat.'

'I wish you'd give me a break. Isolation is hard enough without your comments about my every move. C'mon, Cat, let's make some sourdough.'

Polly pulled out her yeast starter and the baking dish she had been tempted to buy and order online. Since lockdown, making a weekly sourdough had been a satisfying part of her routine. Today she decided on garlic and rosemary.

She turned the radio back on while she prepared the bread mixture and hummed along to John Prine and Iris Dement's *In Spite of Ourselves*. The rarely played ironic love song made her laugh.

'You should get an Alexa,' noted Speech Bubble. *'You could have the song whenever you wanted to. You're so out of touch.'*

Polly shook her head.

Making a final edit to the presentation for Monday, Polly checked the time. '5pm, let's give Jay a try now, Cat, before she heads out for a walk with the dogs. It's 9 o'clock her time.' She clicked the skype button and let it ring, but Jay didn't pick up. 'That's too bad, we haven't spoken in forever.' She was about to shut off the computer when a call came in from Jay.

'Jay, I just called you!' Polly began to sing Happy Birthday.

'I needed a moment hon. Aww thanks, can you turn on your camera?'

'Oh, for goodness' sake, Polly, get with the programme, you stuck tape over it when your boss called, remember?'

'What the heck do you even know about technology, suggesting Alexa earlier?'

'Well apparently more than you do, hon, don't you have an Alexa yet? It's sooo great for music, anytime you want.'

'Sorry, I wasn't talking to you, I know, you're a whiz at this stuff.'

'She's really about as clueless as you are, Polly,' sniped Speech Bubble.

'Oh again, for the last time today please, shut up.'

'Charming Poll doll. Last time you told me to shut up was three years ago, we were loading up my car in BC with your case, you were heading off to roam in the gloaming and I was begging you to stay.'

'Sorry again, I didn't mean you.'

'Ah there you are, why are you sideways on the screen?'

'I don't know ... is that better?' Polly said, re-clipping the detachable camera.

'Yep. Say, you look kinda rumpled, are you okay?'

'Thanks a lot, nice to see you too. Actually, you look a bit rumpled yourself, are you still in bed?'

'I just mean you don't look like your calm self, Polly Brisbane, and yes ma'am, I am still in bed!'

'It's having to stay in isolation again. I caught Covid. I like my own company, just not quite this much of it. Getting dressed seems pointless.'

'Told you, you were letting yourself go,' said Speech Bubble.

'Polly Brisbane, did you just eye roll me?'

'No, not you, my grandmother,' said Polly laughing.

'I didn't know your grandmother was still alive. Does she live with you?'

'She's not actually here, she's dead, it's just her voice ...'

'You hear your grandmother speaking to you?'

'Yes, well, I mean, not her actual voice, just what I think she would say if she were here, she kind of creeps up on me, which has sometimes been helpful.'

'Hon, are you sure you're OK? Has isolation, scotch mist, haggis, and whisky addled your brain?'

'I don't drink whisky, I'm still vegetarian, and Brigadoon was made up. We don't all live in a perpetual state of mist over here. My grandmother's voice popped up when I was fifty, and she's sticking like butter to toast. She's got louder recently.'

'*Too bad I didn't arrive earlier. I would have helped you prevent some marital disasters.*'

'Piss off, you're not helping.'

'Are you being snippy with me or your gran, I can't tell?'

'I was talking to her.'

'Okay ...' Jay's response was interrupted as she heard Cat meow in the background. 'Is that Cat I hear, can I see her?'

'Hang on, I'm just going to give her some food, I'll walk you into the kitchen.' Polly tilted the computer down towards Cat, tucking into her bowl of tuna.

'There she is, she's so lovely, how old now?'

'Eleven. Yep, Cat's keeping me sane,' Polly said, adjusting the computer and heading back to the living room.

'If you say so, Polly, you with your Gran voices and all.'

'*I told you so, Polly. Too much time with Cat,*' Speech Bubble interjected.

'There she goes again, putting me down. Twas always thus.'

'Did you just say "twas always thus"? Have you gone and swallowed a bible, is food that short over there?'

Polly laughed, 'It's so good to see you. Since being cooped up my conversations with Gran, I call her Speech Bubble, have become more intense.'

'You have a name for your dead grandmother who you carry on conversations with? I'm really concerned about you, hon. Since I've been having regular sex, my brain is doing so much better. The fog has lifted. Although there's no chance of an actual romp while you are isolating, you could always order a little something from Amazon, they have a great ...'

Polly leaned her face in closer to the screen and raised her eyebrows.

'Why are you looking at me like that?'

'You didn't tell me you met someone, let alone the ... err, the other thing. Who, where, how?'

'Polly Brisbane, shut your mouth, you look like you're trying to catch flies in it. That's why I haven't had time to call you in forever, sorry. It's been crazy. When we went into another lockdown over here, he kinda moved in. We kept it a secret, just in case, you know. Please don't say anything to Kerry or Sandy, even my girls don't know yet. Six months later, here he still is! I sent him to take a shower and get us both something to eat, so I could speak to you.

'*Cat got your tongue, Polly?*' said Speech Bubble, as Polly wriggled on the chair.

'I don't know what to say. I'm really happy for you, so long as he's ... well, decent, treats you right.'

'Aww, he does. Thanks, Poll doll, too bad there's slim fishing where you are on the Bonnie Banks. I can honestly say this is the best birthday morning I've had in years!'

'How did you fix the other problem, you know, the one I mean? The menopause effect that no one talks about.'

'Ha, it took a while. Seems that old saying, no pain, no gain works. Honestly, it was like sandpaper at first but there are lots of aids out there nowadays, and so long as you find the right someone with imagination and patience.'

Polly put her hands over her ears and pulled a face. 'Stop, way too much information. Maybe I should re-write my bio and put it back on a dating site,' she giggled. 'I'll send it to you, see what you think.'

'*Honestly Polly, you sound about twelve, you're a grown woman, that stage of your life is well and truly over.*'

Polly had a fleeting vision in her mind's eye. It was of her grandmother dressing under one of the tent-like winceyette night gowns she wore all year round. Polly doubted even her grandfather had seen his wife without clothes since they married in Stirling, one hundred years earlier.

'Get off my case, stop being mean. Things have changed a lot.'

'Hearing voices again?'

'Yep. Oh my God, is that him just disappearing out of your ensuite?' Polly's eyes were wide, her mouth hung open as she saw the torso of a tanned male reflection in Jay's mirror.

'Quite the catch, eh, Polly?'

'But isn't he a little …'

'Young?'

'No wonder you look so great rumpled, unlike me.'

Jay leaned into the screen and winked. 'Oh Polly, I feel fantastic.'

'*Face it, Polly, you're as green as grass with envy,*' retorted Speech Bubble.

'No, I'm not!'

'Not what Polly? Is that Gran again? She's pretty annoying, sounds like a bit of a killjoy. Can't you bin her off?'

'Yeah, I should try, you're right. I mean it, Jay, I am really happy for you.'

'*Bin me off! Really Polly, as if. Without me, you'd just go round in circles.*'

Polly heard some dishes rattling on a tray from outside Jay's bedroom. 'I can hear him coming with your breakfast, I'm going to let you get back to whatever it is you're planning, I think I can imagine. Happy Birthday again. Love you. Byeee.'

'Sure, let's chat again soon. Love you too. MMMwa.'

'Another long evening ahead, Cat,' Polly sighed. Come on, you'd better snuggle up with me, while you still can!'

'*Oh dear, another disaster looms.*'

'That's it. You're on mute for the weekend!'

⁂

Since her call with Jay, Polly managed to focus her attention and even keep Speech Bubble quiet. She was eager for the meeting to start on Monday. She washed her hair and finished it with hair tongs. She chose a red top and replaced her PJ bottoms with clean leggings. Then checked her face in the mirror and blotted her lips. The lipstick and eyeliner would make her less washed out on screen, but she didn't want to overdo it. She was singing '*I Will Survive*' when Speech Bubble broke free and interrupted her.

'*Polly Brisbane. Why are you dressed like the proverbial dog's dinner for an online work meeting? Trying to impress anyone special?*'

'None of your business, you're supposed to be on mute.'

'*You'd better watch out, Cat. Looks like when her isolation is over, she's planning on more than just your company.*'

Polly looked at Cat and patted her behind the ears. Cat was just settling down for a tummy rub when the skype call tone started. Michael was early.

'Good morning, Polly, sorry we're a tad early.'

'Not a problem at all, Michael, and *hello,* Nathan, it's *really* nice to see *you* again,' she said smiling confidently as she looked at herself on camera. She didn't look rumpled at all.

Dear John Kerr

——Alison Williamson——

I HOPE TO MAKE JOHN proud today. We both do.

The sea of supporters surge in large waves behind me. As the final chords of Icona Pop's *'I Love It'* ring out, I notice the expressions of the few people that know the song's true significance to the bowling community. They continue the song on even as a new one takes its place. The new artist is given no chance as the crowd drowns out the melodic voice with their brash but impassioned tones.

'I'm John Kerr, I love it. I love it. I'm John Kerr.'

They wipe shy tears from their cheeks, smiling knowingly up to the dimly lit ceiling. John would never miss a bowling tournament.

I wiggle my limbs nervously, removing all the added tension from my joints. Chants and songs blur together. Scotland, England, Ireland, and Wales. The names of different countries ring out from over-eager parents across the alley. The kids grow in age and height as the lane numbers increase. Puberty changes them from excitable innocence to determined experience.

I shake hands with those in my section. I squeeze slightly harder than needed. Their faces twitch in surprise before returning to their usual stoic expressions. Twenty-four games across four disciplines and it all comes down to this. The best of the best in each age category. The practice is over, the friendly banter is gone. It is one bowler and their coach. Speaking of which, where is he?

Returning to my lane, I find my parents emerging from the swallowing crowd. After a decade of practice, they elegantly navigate their way to the front. My dad offers me his usual fist pump with one hand. His other fixes tightly around his 'bowling camera' as he has dubbed it. My mum smiles, raising her pint of beer to me, obviously very glad to have finished with her coaching responsibilities for the tournament.

The shrill beeps and scrapes of the machinery grinding into action brings me back to the task at hand. My last junior tournament and my last chance to win gold for my country. The closing chapter of the book I started at the age of five. My competition move into hushed huddles with their coach. Fingers point and eyes stare in my direction. I overhear the English coach try to motivate his new girls' team. His need for revenge drips from his words. Someone is obviously still bitter about his team's loss last year.

'Now *her*, ladies. She is the one you need to watch out for. Do what you can. Remember she is getting old now.'

Wow. Real mature.

I snort loudly. This disdain is something I have learned to brush off over the years. The childlike sabotage and tricks to try and put people off, instead of just playing the game as it was intended. I take a final glance at the crowd, hunting for my own coaching support. My backup. Someone to protect myself and my equipment from sneaky saboteurs. Why is Jack not here yet? After fifteen years of friendship, you would think I had gotten used to his awful time keeping. John would not be happy with his son in this moment. I stifle a laugh, imagining one of Jack and John's classic father-son arguments. They often started over nothing, included nothing important, and ended with nothing being resolved. Picking up my towel and chalk ball, I close my eyes, remembering John's words to me. The last time he coached me.

⁂

As my score dropped further and further away from my competition I returned to my hard plastic chair. My body moulded into its harsh contours, adopting a slumped and defeated position. With a couple of high two hundred games needed, I watched as my dreams of qualifying seemed to disappear, just as my name did from the leader board. All from my own nervousness and inability to compose myself. A large, calloused hand dropped heavily onto my shoulder. I didn't need to turn round to know my mum had subbed herself out as my coach.

'It's gone, John. I've messed it up.'

I dropped my head into my hands, willing the tears to stay back. I felt his steadying breath move the loose hair from my now messy ponytail. I allowed him to pull me in for a comforting hug.

'Alison, look up at the score.'

I couldn't. Tears fell and disappeared into the tartan of my shorts. A few 'come on' and 'you got this' chants erupted from the Scottish crowd. He squeezed my shoulders tightly, ignoring the attempts of encouragement from behind.

'Block them out. Listen to me. Look up at the score.'

I had too much respect for John to ignore him again. I steadied my breathing. An involuntary hiccup escaped my now salty lips. Wiping away the few stragglers that remained, I thrust my head up grumpily. My eyes locked on my dwindling numbers.

'You know what you need to do.'

'It's impossible John, I haven't shot 240 the whole tournament and now you want me to get two of them?'

'Take it one shot at a time. This is your moment, Alison. Don't let it pass you by, or you'll regret it.'

'It feels like too much. There's too much pressure.'

'Pressure means passion. Which means you want it.'

⁂

Re-opening my eyes, I am assaulted by bright colours from aggressively waving flags. As the games appear on screen, I do a final look for my coach. This is getting old now. I wish I could get John to tell him off somehow, this isn't the punctuality he would want for his son's first coaching gig. I compose myself on the lane, preparing for my first shot of the finals. Picking up the familiar shiny ball, I spin it in one hand. It swishes against the towel in the other, cleaned with expert precision. I stare down the daunting white and red striped soldiers. With every deep breath they shrink in stature. Drying out my wet palm with my chalk ball and the uncomfortably warm fan air, I wriggle and stretch my fingers to their limits. With a glance back to my parents, I use their encouraging smiles to push me forward into my first shot. I don't know who is more annoyed with Jack in this moment; myself, my parents, or John.

Taking a step onto the glistening wooden approach, the sound disappears from behind me. My own breath and heartbeat take over my senses, their steady rhythm provides a metronome for my body to move to. The preparation is done, muscle memory takes over. My body moves with fluidity towards the start of the lane. Every movement happens on its correct step. With the final sliding step, the ball elegantly removes itself from my digits and begins its path down the lane. In that moment, when the ball hits the lane and until it hits the pins, the world stands still and only that sound matters.

As the ball drives into the pins, a crescendo of noise comes erupting from the crowd and crushes into my ear drums. With no soldiers left in the battle, I turn around and welcome the applause. A loud and steady clap separates from the rest, my coach has decided to arrive. He looks at me sheepishly, hoping if he can look apologetic enough, I won't shout at him. After all these years he knows me too well. I run up to Jack engaging in our obligatory 'try and hurt the other person's hand' high five.

'One – nil to you. Sorry.'

He shakes his hand rapidly, trying to remove the stinging prickle from his skin. I snort, happy I won the round.

'Well, you're supposed to be here before I throw my first ball. I don't know if I want to keep you as my coach after that.'

'I wouldn't blame you. Although I do have a good reason. Want to know now or after?'

I always hate when Jack says that. He knows I have no patience. I follow his eyeline up to the crowd, finding the judgemental faces of the Scottish committee. The two older ladies sip their tepid Chardonnay proudly, despite signing a contract to say they would stay sober. They stare sourly at us whispering to each other.

'What have we done this time then?'

'They don't want me to coach you. They think that we're dating and it's unprofessional.'

I roll my eyes hard enough that even the two ladies can see it through their misty wine glasses. It is not the first time we have been accused of this. The inability to see a boy and girl as just friends is baffling and something I didn't expect to face in my twenties.

'Oh my god, what do they expect me to do? Start mounting you in the middle of the bowling alley?'

'Don't know, but they banned me from coming down here.'

'Wait, what do you mean they banned you? You're here now.'

'They said if I came down here, I couldn't coach for Scotland again.'

Jack's eyes move to the floor. I watch as he dances his left foot around the worn tile beneath us. A nervous twitch he developed after his dad died. He does it whenever he is thinking of him. I place my hand on his shoulder, a gust of air is huffed in our direction from my impatient opponent. She shuffles loudly around the playing area, obviously hoping to annoy me into taking my next shot.

'Go back up there. Say you were just letting me know the story. I will pull my dad down to coach me.'

His eyes shoot up, any evidence of grief is gone. He angrily shakes his head and points a solitary digit sharply at the tipsy ladies behind him.

'They can't deny someone coaching with no evidence other than their old-fashioned opinions.'

My opponent taps her broken acrylic nail against her Casio watch. She searches for her coach; he has already gone hunting for a tournament official. Eager to make me bowl quicker so I don't upset their practiced rhythm.

'But Jack, this is something you've wanted for a while. Something you're doing for your dad.'

'My dad never left you on your own, so why would I?'

I smile softly at him, nodding at his encouragement. He burls me round on the spot pushing me towards the lane. I stumble with the momentum and knock my opponent backwards into the hard plastic chairs. I offer her a hand, but she turns her head away from me. I hear the beginnings of unkind words escape in whispers. Choosing to ignore her pettiness, I begin my pre-shot routine. I glance back at Jack's cheeky grin almost bursting with a quick-witted comment he wants to get out. I raise my eyebrows as a blessing, and he struggles to say his one liner without it becoming inaudible giggles.

'Now don't make me look bad, I'm sticking my neck out for you here.'

I laugh as I step onto the approach, steadying my hilarity to focus on the task at hand. A smile forms as I hear our encouraging phrase to one another:

'I will always be here for you. You got this.'

⁂

We finally pulled up to the church after a five-hour drive down to England.

I wished I hadn't worn my black clothes in the stifling July weather, as I was sandwiched in the middle seat of the hotbox car.

I wished my dad had decided to get a new car instead of claiming that 'the windows down' did just as good a job as air conditioning.

I wished that John hadn't gotten cancer and died.

I stickily separated myself from the others in the car. I smoothed the one or two wrinkles that the heat hadn't gotten to on my dress and put on my brave façade. John had fought cancer for two years before it took him. He continued coaching, continued his support, and continued his fight until his last breath.

That day was for us all to say goodbye, but for me, it was also a day that I had to get my best friend through. We turned the corner as a group and were met with a mix of familiar and unfamiliar faces. Everyone locked eyes with everyone, and everyone shared the same expression as everyone. The lack of conversation hung heavy in the humid air. People whispered in their small groups. Some shared memories of John, some had a basic catch-up conversation after not seeing each other since the last big event, and some continued to gossip about the choice in venue and other things, the gravity of the situation obviously lost on them.

Seconds felt like hours and minutes like days as we stood baking on the church's front steps. If spirits were better, I would have made a joke about God knowing I wasn't baptised, but it didn't seem like the right time. Or place for that matter. The crunching of gravel indicated the arrival of the funeral party. A sleek black hearse rolled sombrely into view. The sun bounced brightly off the bonnet, it sent beams of dazzling light into different directions.

As the family car stopped in front of us, there was a brief pause before the door swung open. Jack's mum stepped out first, clutched onto her own mother for support. She drowned her mother in her grief, relying on the elderly woman to practically lift her inside the church. My eyes did not remain fixed on them for long. My reason for being there was still hidden in the safety of the car.

He emerged from the shadowed interior, his gaze drifting across the group in front of him. Many tried to say, 'sorry for your loss' or to mouth 'are you okay'. His eyes did not remain on them long, he looked over and under the wave of bodies as he searched. As he found my parents his expression turned quizzical and a moment of hurt flashed across his features. Did he honestly think I wouldn't come? My mum pointed swiftly in my direction and Jack's eyes locked onto mine. His expression changed to one of relief. He remained like that for a moment. I offered him a soft smile, no words.

What do you say to someone in this situation? Well wishes and condolences feel forced and fake. They hold no promises, no understanding, no impact. They are there to make the mourners feel they have helped the family, when in reality it only helped themselves.

Jack broke our gaze and reached in to bring out his younger sister. He boosted her up onto his hip and she hid her face from the crowd. Buried deep into Jack's neck, her broken sobs rung out through the open air. Silence followed her tears.

The funeral continued on in the way funerals normally do. John's life was told to us on two sides of A5 paper and a few hymns were sung that had nothing to do with him or his life. The funeral was average. The priest chose to focus more on us donating to improve the seats in his church than the coffin laid out decoratively behind him. I sat a few rows back, my eyes mainly fixed onto the back of my best friend's head. John's coffin began to move behind the curtain and Jack's younger sister was shuffled to her mum for support.

The movement of the coffin was halted as Jack rose from his seat in the pew. He politely excused himself and exited the row. I thought he was going to leave. My mind begged him to stay, knowing he would regret it later. He walked to the row I was sitting in. Politely excusing himself again he manoeuvred his way through before he plopped himself down next to me and grasped my hand tightly in his.

He said nothing, just stared at the coffin containing his father. The gathering's eyes were fixated on us and through the silence no-one dared to breathe. I focused on the priest as he looked for an indication of what to do next. I squeezed Jack's hand strongly in my own, bringing my other down to shield it from onlookers.

'You can continue, sir.' I didn't know if I should say 'father' or 'priest' but knew it was best to be polite.

The service finished and Jack remained attached to my hand. I excused us from the larger gathering to a shaded woodland area at the back of the hotel where the wake was held. A sturdy bench offered us respite from our grief. As we sat, Jack removed his hand from mine and wrapped it around my waist. I felt his body begin to shake, and he mirrored his sister's earlier actions. His sobs racked his slender frame and I held him to me. We sat like that for hours. I ushered well-wishers away. His mum came out to check on him. She mouthed me a thanks as she made her way back inside, careful not to disturb.

'I'll always be here for you. You got this.'

⚓

The ball spirals into the pins for my last strike, the pins fall out of fear. The cracking whip noise resonates over the now quiet bowling alley. Cameras flash at me and Jack as we stand for obligatory photos. I talk to him through grimaced teeth, keeping my picture-perfect smile on my face.

'Sorry I couldn't win it for you mate. I tried.'

'Don't be sorry, need something to work towards when I coach you next.'

I playfully punch his shoulder, knocking him off balance and stumbling into the uncomfortable hard plastic chairs. I seem to be good at doing that to people. Laughter and sniggers break out from behind the lenses as the flashes keep going. I offer him a hand and drag him back onto his feet.

'You know what I mean. We make a good team. Not as good as you and my dad, mind you.'

I always like when Jack talks about his dad. He often hides it. I pull him into a hug, and he bends to bury his head into my neck like he did at the funeral. He hugs me back, happy for the comfort surrounding him even though his dad has been gone for a few years now.

'You think your dad would be proud of us today?'

'I think so.'

'I think so too.'

Let it Be Seen

——Jennifer Syme——

Move within, and
Turn off the noise of the world.
Know that your inner self
Is worthy of more
Care and attention.

Listen to its quiet voice
Let its strength guide you to
New spaces,
New pleasures, and
New adventures.

Softly, gently, let it out.
Its mask removed
Breathing fresh, clean air
At last.
Let it smile.
Let it be heard.
Let it be seen.

The Stars Are Out Tonight

——Jennifer Syme——

HANNAH JUMPED AS ONE OF the many machines surrounding her dad's hospital bed gave a strident, long-lasting beep. It was the sound television or film would use to show the patient was no more. She looked across the bed. Her two sisters were staring back at her. Their pale, exhausted faces with matching 'O' shaped mouths.

A nurse came in and said, 'Sorry, that's just the machine, I'll sort it for you.' She gave them a sympathetic smile as she turned to leave again.

Hannah felt like a freshly caught fish, gasping for breath in alien surroundings. Her legs pushed her to stand as the desire to get out of this room overrode everything else. There wasn't enough air.

'I'm sorry, I can't do this. I can't, I just can't.'

'It's okay, Han, you go. You're shattered,' Fiona, her eldest sister, said.

'Don't worry, we'll stay,' Sarah added.

Fiona nodded. 'We can take it in turns if we need a break.'

Hannah bent and kissed her dad's cool forehead. 'Cheerio,' she whispered, 'Cheerio Dad.'

Her words caught in the back of her throat, and she gave a tiny sob. One part of her mind, the one that had stuck its fingers in its ears and hummed whenever a doctor tried to explain that her dad was dying, was saying goodbye until the next day. As if all was normal. The other part, the one that had understood the consultant, that part was in pieces. That part of her knew this was the last time she would see him.

She stumbled out of the ICU and down the corridor to the waiting room, where her two brothers-in-law had spent most of the day.

'The men never stay,' her sister Sarah, a nurse herself, had said when they had excused themselves after an hour of hovering. 'It's always the women who sit by the bedside.'

Hannah, Fiona, and Sarah had sat there for eight hours, stroking their father's forehead and hands with soft cloths which had a few drops of lavender oil on them. The nursing staff had suggested they bring favourite scents, books to read to him, or soothing music. Their dad had grown lavender in his garden, and in the summer, the bushes heaved with buzzing bees and silent, flitting butterflies.

Although Hannah had only been nine when her mother died, she remembered helping her make bunches of lavender for the house or to dry for cupboards. Her dad had kept the practice going. He said it reminded him of their mother and, for Hannah, it was the scent of home. When they weren't using the lavender cloth, they held his hands, talking in quiet voices. They only moved to turn the cassette over when it finished. They played his favourite opera, *La Boheme*, on repeat. It would be a long time before any of them could listen to it again.

Now, Hannah burst into the waiting room, pushing the door too hard in her rush. She struggled to free herself from the plastic apron they had to wear in the ICU. Its knot was tight, impossible to loosen. She tugged in vain before finally ripping it off.

Fiona's husband Douglas stood up, about to speak, but Hannah beat him to it. 'I need to go, I can't ...'

Then the tears came, and she felt herself being enfolded by his arms and hugged close.

'Come on, I'll get you a taxi to take you to Ben's.'

Their brother, Ben, had already left. He was unwell himself, having had major surgery after a car accident. He needed a supportive chair, and his medicine, so he had headed home a couple of hours earlier. As she stood silently with Douglas in the lift, Hannah thought of Ben at home, with only his pain and his pills for company. What could he be doing but sitting and thinking, waiting for that phone call? He'd had his accident at the same time as their dad had taken ill. He hadn't been able to see him over the last few months, which had distressed Ben so much he'd threatened to discharge himself.

There were a couple of taxis waiting at the hospital rank. Douglas spoke to the driver as Hannah settled into the back seat. Hannah leaned her head on the window, looking through her own reflection and out at the moonlit fields, and the leaves falling from the wind-whipped trees. Her eyes were dry now, and she became aware that the heavy weight that had sat in her stomach for the past few days, making it impossible to eat, had gone. She was starving. Her stomach rumbled to prove it.

She sat up and glanced at the driver. He flicked his eyes to look at her in the rear-view mirror.

'Not far now, hen,' he said.

Hannah nodded and checked the dashboard clock; it was 10:40 p.m. No wonder she was hungry. She had a vague memory of nibbling on a piece of toast that morning. It felt like a lifetime ago.

She sat back in the seat and looked out the window again. This time she noticed the Big Dipper. Right there, in front of her. She smiled to herself as the memories came, of herself as a small child, maybe 6 years old, standing on the steps of their house on a dark, crisp autumn evening. They were most likely going to the library or the cinema. The pictures were an occasional treat, but the library was a weekly trip for her and her dad. They went every Friday, always coming home via the café where they got the others' sweetie orders—midget gems, 'Russian' toffees, nougat—all in their little paper bags. She would sit on the back seat, clutching the bag of sweets and her books. Friday was the best night of the week. In the summer, they sometimes got ice cream; the deliciously soft, white Italian gelato scooped directly from the churner into the waiting cone. Sometimes as a '99' or drizzled with red syrup that made her hands sweet and sticky.

That night was the first time she could recall noticing the stars.

'Look!' she'd said, and her dad had squatted down to her level and pointed out the Big Dipper and then the Little Dipper. He had used his finger to draw the outline. It had amazed her that someone had made drawings with the stars. She had thought of him as the big one, and she was the little one.

For a long time, she'd thought her dad must've known all the stars. He always had a name for her when she asked—Orion's Belt, Dylan, Ziggy, Jumping Dog.

Later, her sisters and brother had told her in their usual teasing way that he'd made most of them up. It didn't matter to Hannah. They became her 'north', something she checked for wherever she went.

As they neared Ben's town, she looked for the Little Dipper, but the streetlights and houses blocked her view.

'Here we are, hen,' said the taxi driver as he turned into Ben's driveway. 'Your man back there paid the fare.'

The front door opened as the taxi reversed away, and Ben stood silhouetted against the hall light. He was leaning against the doorframe and holding something in his other hand. As she walked down the path, he waved, and she realised it was a phone.

'He's gone, Hannah,' Ben said as she got to the door. 'They called just now.'

His voice wobbled, and she stepped up the two steps to hug him. He had to keep holding the doorway as he didn't have his stick, but he held her close with his free arm. She could feel the phone still in his hand, its dull edge against her back.

'What time?' she said, her voice muffled against his thick jumper.

'10:40 was the official time.' Ben answered, stepping back, 'The others felt the same as you and left. But he wasn't alone, the nurses were there, and they had the music on. The nurses said sometimes patients hang on while the family is there, so once people leave, they slip away.'

Hannah felt her stomach dip, 'They left him? They said they would wait. I would've stayed.' She took a deep breath, trying to push her anger away, 'I just needed a break. I don't like thinking of him alone.'

Ben nodded, 'Yeah, I know what you mean, but sometimes it's for the best, like the nurse said. And everyone is done in. It's been a long day.'

He turned and started limping down the hallway, using the walls and occasional furniture for support.

'Come on, I'll get you some food. You must be starving. There's rolls leftover from earlier, with cheese or ham, or a tin of soup. What do you fancy?'

'A roll sounds good,' Hannah said, 'With cheese; do you have any pickle?'

As she followed Ben down to the kitchen, she spotted her little overnight bag on the stairs. She had dumped it there earlier before they'd gone to the hospital. Seeing it now, it looked like something a stranger had left behind.

Ben busied himself making some cheese and pickle rolls while she filled the kettle to make a pot of tea. Hannah was pouring them each a cup when the doorbell rang.

'That'll be Fiona, Sarah, and the guys,' Ben said.

'I'll get it,' Hannah said, putting the teapot down and heading down the hall to get the door.

Soon they were all sitting around the kitchen table, eating the soft, white rolls and drinking hot, sweet tea. Fiona and Sarah on one side, opposite Neil and Douglas. Ben at the top end so he could stretch his leg out, and Hannah off to one side, perched on one of the high stools at the kitchen island. They talked in quiet voices about the surreal day that felt like a week and what they needed to do now.

Ben produced a bottle of Glenmorangie, one of her dad's favourites, and poured them all large glasses with a wee dribble of water. He stood up and held his glass high, swirling the whisky around.

'To the funniest, kindest,' he stopped and looked around. 'You say some.'

The rest of them all stood too and shouted out words, raising their glasses high.

'Silliest.'

'Fez-wearing,' Hannah said, but was drowned out by Neil's louder, 'Generous.' She opened her mouth to repeat it, but closed it again as the others continued, yelling the words now.

'Story-telling.'

'Loving.'

'Stubborn.'

'Protective.'

There was a brief silence, and Hannah said, 'Fez-wearing.'

Ben raised his glass again, 'To Dad.'

'To Dad.' They all chorused before sitting back down.

'Thanks, Ben! That was lovely,' said Fiona, wiping tears off her cheeks.

'What's with the fez-wearing?' Neil asked, 'I don't recall that.'

Hannah laughed, 'I got him a fez for his birthday, from a Laurel and Hardy shop when we were on holiday. I was about 15, and we both loved the *Sons of the Desert* film where they have the fezzes. I was sorry, though, when he turned up to collect me from a party wearing the damn fez. My friends thought he was great; their dads were so boring. They dragged him in and begged him to do his Egyptian dance. He'd done it at my party. Of course, Dad was delighted to perform, fez still on his head. Most people were laughing and dancing, but I was dying, because Rob Kerr, who I fancied and had heard might fancy me too, was shouting 'nutter'. She took the whisky bottle Ben was passing around and filled her own glass, 'Ach well, Rob was a boring fart.'

As the glasses were refilled, Ben told them how he'd seen their dad doing the transformation scene from an old *Dr Jekyll and Mr Hyde* film, pre-CGI.

'He was doing it in the mirror, contorting himself,' said Ben, 'He did it well. When he saw me behind him, he jumped and said, what did I think? So, I said it was good.' Ben took a sip of his drink. 'He said that he scared himself the first time he did it.'

'God, I could just see him getting the fear from his own reflection, what an imagination he had. Remember all those bedtime stories he used to make up for us? The one about the magic book the kids could jump into was my favourite,' said Sarah.

'Oh yes,' Fiona said, 'and the jungle one. I always hoped he'd write them down.' She sipped her drink. 'Do any of you remember my hair disaster of 1975?'

Ben snorted, 'Oh my God! Yes! That half-perm, half-mullet thing.'

Fiona stuck her tongue out at him. 'For some reason, I didn't have my key, so I rang the bell. Dad answered, and he just said "yes?" and pretended he didn't know me.'

She gave a little hiccup that was half a cry. 'I burst into tears and yelled I was going to shave my head. He said, "come on." Took me upstairs to the bathroom, got out his clippers, and said, "How do you want it?" Got me laughing eventually.'

'You should've let him,' said Ben, 'I've probably got photos of that permlet somewhere.'

'Permullet,' snorted Douglas.

'Mullperm, no, Mulpermlet,' shouted Sarah.

'Oh, fuck off!' said Fiona, laughing, 'You better not have any photos, Ben.'

'Ach, have some more whisky, Fi. Relax, all the photos are at his house.'

'He didn't take many back then, just when Hannah was born.'

They all looked round at Hannah, nodding.

'That's not true. I've not seen many of me either,' Hannah said.

'Ach away, he doted on you, his "Happy Hannah".' Fiona took her refilled glass back from Ben. 'He was always taking your photo.' She took a large slurp of her whisky. 'He filled your head with such nonsense too, remember you thought he knew all the stars in the sky, you wrote a story about it for school.'

'I got a gold star,' Hannah nodded, 'I was so proud, it was my first one for story-telling. Then, when I said at the tea table, you all laughed and shouted that he didn't; he only knew three. And teased him for telling me. He was proud of that gold star anyway, he told me.'

She looked around at them. 'You were always teasing him for the very things that made him, HIM. And it didn't matter to me that he only knew three proper constellations. Like any of you know any at all. It was still our thing, mine and him. The Big Dipper, Little Dipper, and Orion. He always said to me, look for them, they're always there, always the same.'

She heard her voice wobble as she struggled not to cry, 'And I wouldn't have left him alone if you'd all gone first. I'd have stayed.'

There was a silence, Hannah sipped her drink, avoiding eye contact with the others.

'Oh Hannah, that's not fair. We were all tired,' Sarah said, her voice shaking, 'and you are the most like him; you had a different relationship. But our teasing was just fun. He knew that.' She stopped and looked at Fiona, who took her hand and nodded, tears falling onto her cheeks as she did.

Hannah stood, swigging the last of her drink without looking at them, 'I'm going to bed. I feel like I've been awake for a week.'

She fell into the single bed she had been allocated. It was her niece Sally's bedroom, the walls covered with ponies and popstars. The children were all having a sleep over with friends for the weekend.

The Big Dipper came into her mind, and she thought how strange it was she'd felt hungry right at the time her dad had passed away. In a way, it made her feel better, that there was still some deep father and youngest daughter link.

This made her think of the way the evening had ended. She gave a small groan, her normal reaction would be to apologise, to keep the peace, but not this time. What she'd said was true; if they had said they would leave, then Hannah would've stayed. She rolled onto her back and stared at the ceiling, letting her mind drift into happier memories, of stars and adventures.

A holiday to the north of Scotland and the islands came to mind. The pitch-black nights revealed more stars than she had ever imagined possible. She had sat with her then-boyfriend, the two of them wrapped in blankets from their rented cottage, smoking pot and drinking beers. They had sat for hours gawping at the sky, gasping when something, a shooting star, she said, zipped across. She knew some were probably satellites but didn't care.

On her gap-year travels, she had gone to Australia and New Zealand and had been confused by the different night sky. She hadn't expected to feel so lost. It had felt like she was on another planet. Daytime was okay; she enjoyed her casual jobs and evenings with friends, but at night she felt anxious and unable to sleep. The moon is the same, she whispered to herself as she looked out the window at an unfamiliar sky.

One day a package arrived for her at the hostel in Cairns. A book-shaped parcel with a Sydney postmark. There was a note attached to the gift-wrapped item inside. '*Darling Hannah, I called this shop, and they are sending you their best book on Southern stars. I hope it helps. Enjoy the rest of your wonderful adventure. Lots of love, Dad.*' Inside the parcel was a book about the Southern sky, with beautiful images of stars to spot. She found the equivalent easy-to-spot constellations and looked for them instead. It helped, but it wasn't the same.

Once she'd crossed back over the Equator to Thailand under the familiar Northern stars, she could feel herself relax. On her first nights there, she sat outside the beach hostel, ignoring the parties that were going on along the beach, and looked up, raising a beer to the Big Dipper.

Now, her dad was gone.

Tears filled her eyes again as she turned her head to look out the window. There was a gap between the curtains, giving her a glimpse of the sky. She reached up to open the curtain wider so she could see better. As she pulled it to one side, she smiled at what she saw in the sky, right in front of her.

The Big Dipper.

The stars were always there, always the same.

The Bad Date Chronicles: Will I Ever Find My Prince Charming? A Generation Addicted to Online Dating.

—— *Chloe Craig* ——

HEY FRIENDS, I COME TO you today with the all-important question … What is it about online dating? Why do we all do it?

What's happened to meeting people in a pub, or being set up with someone that one of your friends thinks you'll 'really hit it off' with? I don't know about you, but I find the cheesy bios and conversation starters a little bit too much – you know, the lines about whether pineapple belongs on pizza or if Ross and Rachel were really on a break … because that one just screams originality. Yet somehow, they work. The next thing, you're a week deep into conversations with the guy and you've agreed to go on an actual date.

Online dating leads to brunch dates, dinner dates and those 'let's hang out at my place' dates *insert the eye rolling emoji here* and if we're going to be honest with ourselves… what's the success rate of any of these? Like 10%? I honestly don't know why any of us do it anymore. We put ourselves through this process just to be let down time and time and time again?

I'm gonna tell you about one of my most recent dates. One that definitely didn't go to plan … now Brad, he really takes the cake for the most uneventful date ever! His profile picture said that he was the 'blonde hair blue eyes, knows that he's pretty type'. I'm not one to judge though, so I decided to give him a chance. I dread to think about how much gel he'd used in that perfectly blonde hair of his, but there was absolutely no chance of it falling out of place. Each line that made the quiff style had its own exact spot. It was obvious which one of us had spent the most time getting ready for the date. I couldn't tell this from his profile picture, but he was quite tall too. Looks-wise, he had the whole package. He was the type of guy that tries to dress a certain way without having to spend the big bucks. His suit could have been from Armani, but it was more like a cheaper Next version! So, he's the try-hard type – oh fab!

He picked me up in his car from the pub just around the corner from my flat. Remember lovelies, it's always better to be safe than sorry – too many creeps around nowadays to take a chance. It was some sort of sports car that I didn't care for. All I knew for sure was that it wasn't a Ferrari. When he arrived and got out of the car to open the door for me, my first thought was 'how nice', but oh boy I was wrong.

'She's new, don't want to risk any scratches,' he said. As he looked down at my recently manicured nails. He walked back around to his side. His slow slide into the interior made me nauseous. Legs spread, ready and waiting, he was carefully caressing the gearstick as the engine began to purr. Why was I there? He didn't need to go on this date with me, he had his car.

It got worse! He'd already decided on the restaurant. 'Vineyard On the Wharf' – a really fancy restaurant in central London. Even the name sounds pretentious. When we got there, he was greeted by the waiter, by his first name no less.

'Brad, how lovely to see you again.'

I'm not sure if Brad is blind to how people really feel about him, but the strained smile that came along with the waiter's response definitely told me that he was lying. All of the waiters were wearing a waistcoat and tie and freshly steamed trousers that were practically stuck to their legs! I hated this place already. Brad wasn't joking when he told me that he 'knows this charming little spot'. I had a feeling that his regular presence was tolerated by the staff simply because he seems like the type that would go all out, no expense spared. We hadn't even sat down, and I already felt so out of place.

We were taken to his 'usual' table, and I couldn't help but roll my eyes. It was in the very far corner of the restaurant, out of earshot and pretty much out of sight from anyone else. We were under a spotlight of low, warm toned lights, for the 'ambiance' as he called it. Oh, and it was right beside the toilets! So, no chance of an easy escape route for me then. I started to feel an overwhelming sense that I wasn't the first and I certainly wouldn't be the last woman he'd put on this charade for. If he thought that this was going to impress me, then I really do feel sorry for him. I knew at that moment that this was going to be the longest and most painful experience of my entire life.

'I'll take a glass of my usual red and the lady will have a glass of the Chardonnay.'

'Erm, I'm actually not much of a white wine drinker Brad. I prefer rosé if you don't mind?'

'Oh, but this is some of the best white wine in the city! Trust me, it won't disappoint.' If his taste in wine is anything like his taste in restaurants, then I was absolutely going to be disappointed. I don't think I need to tell you all how much I didn't love being told by a man what I would like. I took a sip just to make him happy and I had to force myself to swallow it.

Brad proceeded to order things off the menu that he had 'tried and tested multiple times' ... oh lucky me! Sushi finger rolls and some kind of lobster puffs. I was sat thinking 'Oh God, please no! What's the deal with this guy? Who in their right mind thinks that it's a good idea to have finger food on a first date?' Especially when everyone knows that you should go for something safe like chicken and veg. I suppose that would be out of the question for a thirty-something uptight, pretentious accountant though. Surely picking the wine for me was bad enough, but he had to choose the food as well. I've never had lobster before, so I was unsure about that, but then Brad insisted on pointing out the tank that they were in. Still alive and looking far too calm for my liking. My mind was already made up. I tried it even though I didn't want to. God forbid I offended him. I made sure to only try it once and then I stuck to the sushi rolls. The whole time we were eating, I made a point to use chopsticks since we were having fish courses, but much to my surprise, Brad decided to eat with his hands. I couldn't help but think about the lingering smell and what that would do to him ... he'd leave it all over his car, but I expect that would just increase the sexual tension between him and that awful tin box. I needed to get out of this, it was officially my worst first date ever!

I've never known someone who had the ability to talk so much about themselves and not even think to ask the other person anything. Although, if I had been given the chance to speak, I'm not sure what I'd have asked.

'This is the most perfect red wine I've ever tasted; I never get red from anywhere else. Sometimes I order an extra bottle just to take it home with me. I come here a lot too, so the owner lets me buy some of their stock of it as well whenever I want to.' What a shock! He poured himself another glass and that's when he realised that mine was still practically full. I decided to take the plunge and have another sip. Gross. So dry. Much like this bloody conversation – if you could even call it that.

'Is there something wrong with the Chardonnay love?'

'Well, like I said, I'm not really much of white wine drinker, so it's just taking some getting used to.' I refrained from making it obvious with my face, but Brad referring to me as 'love' made my whole body squirm. There was no way that would be happening again.

Poor guy, I felt sorry for him in a way; he's too in love with himself to realise that he's gonna be a car-obsessed, wine-loving, pretentious bachelor for the rest of his life. Just when I thought the conversation couldn't get any worse, he then decided to talk *at me* for ten minutes about his goddamn car. I'd respond with a nod of my head or a 'ahh, uh huh.'

'She's a really smooth runner, an absolute babe to handle.'

That's the only thing that you're going to be handling for a long time.

The train hasn't left the station in a long time, if you get my drift, but even I'm not that desperate. I'd jump at the chance for some action, just not with him. I imagine Brad would probably treat me like his car … one slip in and it would be over, no build up needed. A wild ride in his eyes.

'Bread, milk …' I'd started to distract myself by thinking about my shopping list. Why do guys feel the need to sexualise their cars? That was the final straw, I couldn't put myself through this anymore. I'd sent Laurie our trusty 'one for the list, not one for the lip' text – we'd been using it for years. Whichever one of us received the message had to call the other immediately. Brad was too busy talking about himself to realise that I'd taken my phone out. Laurie was having a major 'fashion crisis' and was in desperate need of my help. This excuse couldn't have been more Laurie if she'd tried, but I was thankful that it worked. Two hours of my life that I'll never get back. I told myself that night that that was the last time I'd go on a date with a guy whose only personality trait was him having a 'cool car.'

It seems that I've started my own tradition. Every painstakingly boring date that I've endured and added to my mental tally has ironically ended in me dancing around my living room, drinking copious amounts of rosé wine (much to Brad's dismay) singing the lyrics to the chorus of Harry Nilsson's 'Without You'. At least Bridget Jones would be proud. *'I can't live, if living is without you.'* And no, Brad, I'm not singing about you ... In this instance, let's just say for my own sake that I'm referring to the wine.

That's just one example of an awful date that I've had. But what about the ones that happened when you found yourself in a moment of desperation and swiped right on someone's Tinder profile without even really thinking about it? Let's not kid ourselves here girls ... we've all been there. It usually goes a little something like this ... it's a Friday night. You're home alone, a little too much wine (rosé in my case) has been consumed and you're feeling sorry for yourself because you've realised that it's been a hot minute since you were given any sort of attention. Take it from someone with way too much experience! Yes, I'm admitting that. I don't think any of you who follow me here will be shocked, though.

We've all become so reliant on dating apps. The incessant swiping of left and right has become such a normal part of our daily lives. I don't know about you, but one discovery that I've made is just how unimaginative most men are. Of course, they'd never be able to accept how very unoriginal and *similar* their profiles are to every other man, so we'll let them believe that they're all different. I've lost count of how many profile pictures I've seen of guys holding a dog ... Is there a secret list of requirements for male dating profiles that we haven't seen, with one stating: 'Must have at least one photo which includes a dog?'

Don't get me wrong, I know that a lot of people are susceptible to a cute dog (I'm one of them), but the number of times that you find out that the dog doesn't even belong to them is just downright sad. It's all the same: 'I love the outdoors, long walks in nature are the best', 'I love pizza and I want to find someone that I can spend nights cuddled on the sofa with,' which actually translates to: 'I want someone that I can Netflix and Chill with.' I'm almost thirty for crying out loud! Most days I'm in bed before 10pm – there's no time or energy left for me to want to 'Netflix and Chill.'

I've discovered that even though their bios rhyme off all the same usual stuff, most guys also fit into one of five different categories: The Tory – you know the one I'm talking about. The type that went to a private school, thanks to 'mummy and daddy' and must let everyone know that. Their wardrobe consists of suits, ties, and stripy shirts (probably from somewhere like Ralph Lauren). They'll have a Politics degree, and their entire personality hangs on the belief that the sun shines out of Boris Johnson's backside.

The Footballer (but the 'I could have gone pro, if I didn't injure myself' type). The best bit is when you tell them that you 'don't really support anyone'. Which is our way of saying that we don't care about football, and then they reply with: 'Well, what team does your dad support', like that's gonna make any difference!

Then you've got the one that is very serious about his Spotify playlists (he listens to Indie music because he thinks that it'll make him seem more 'edgy'.) Most of his messages consist of song suggestions by some obscure band that you've never heard of, usually from somewhere like Iceland. You tell him that you're busy right now and will listen to them later, but never do. I grew up listening to the classics like Whitney Houston, Queen, and ABBA, not Indie bands that have some weird name like 'Burnt Skin' or something.

There's always that one guy that classes himself as a 'traveller' as well. When really, he did one summer backpacking through Europe, and it was like five years ago. He wanted to 'find' himself, but really, he spent six weeks getting absolutely sloshed on cheap Spanish vodka and sleeping with anyone that even looked his way.

Finally, there's the 'I'm (almost) 6 foot' guy. I don't know why guys lie about their height on dating apps ... more than likely it's because they think they can get away with it. Just an FYI, if a guy says that he's either 6 foot or nearly 6 foot – the truth is that he's actually 5'8", but he just doesn't want to admit that he's 'small'.

If the shoe was on the other foot, I'm sure guys would tell us how much women fit into categories too. It's pretty obvious that I'm 100% a representation of a type of woman: the kind who drinks too much wine, spends their time wishing that they were in a rom-com and hoping that some guy will eventually come and sweep them off their feet. I'm a Bridget Jones at heart. I can't deny that that's who I am, but I'm okay with it. I'm not ashamed of it and for any of you girls out there who are the same, you don't have to be either. So, I'm living in a world full of 'what if's' and possibly a lot of false pretences, so what?

I think it comes down to the question of 'What do we really want?' Is it true that we long to find a guy who wants to settle down with us and start a family, or do we just want someone that we can have fun with, without having to think about any kind of commitments? When you get to your thirties and you haven't had either yet, it's totally fine to have absolutely no idea. Maybe you want to experience both … there's nothing wrong with that. We shouldn't go out there looking for exactly what we want because that's when things start to go wrong, and we end up disappointed. At the end of the day, we're living in a world where men have a lot of control over how our relationships go, especially when it comes down to the casual flings. I say, have fun with it! Don't spend your days worrying. Just because there are people around you starting families and getting married, does not mean that you have to. We'll find the right person for us when it's the right time. This may seem like a lot of advice for you all, but it's actually something that I need to listen to myself as well. If you are the kind of person that wants a genuine, honest guy, then that's fine too. We're not asking for much, are we?

I'm sure that there are people out there who enjoy online dating and I'm not saying that it's a bad experience for everyone, but I think it's time that I took a very long break from it. I'm tired of hanging around on these apps and expecting something different to happen when it's just the same wasted experience time and time again. I'm making a pact with myself this very second that the next time I meet a guy, it will be in person and if that takes me a while then I'm okay with that.

Love wisely, my lovelies.

Your favourite hopeless romantic, M x

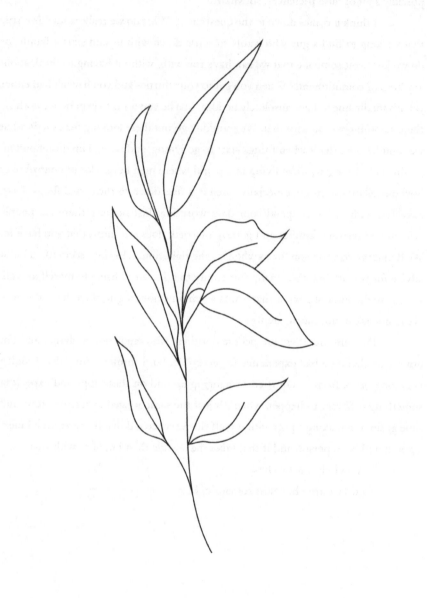

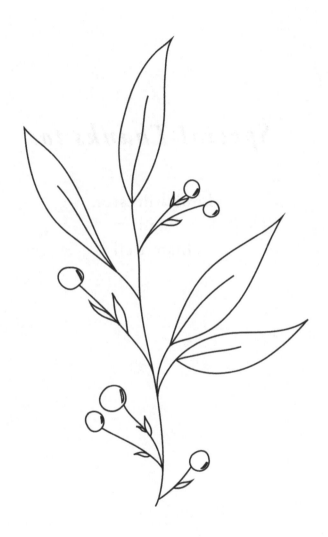

Special Thanks to:

Louisa Preston
—and—
Liam Bell

Solas

—Contributors—

Chris Appleyard
Genoviev Aviles
Marianne L. Berghuis
Morgan Carmichael
Chloe Craig
Emily Crawford
Ruth Irons
Dorcy Jaffray
Hayli McClain
Callum McGee
Morgan MacVaugh
Liza Miles
Trish Stafanovic
Jennifer Syme
Ashleigh Marie Symms
David Toplif
Matthew Weston
Alison Williamson

Stryvling Press
—2022 Team—

Project Manager Lead:
Catherine Albano

Assistant Project Manager:
Marlee Perez

Editorial Lead:
Siobhan Hamilton

Editorial Assistant:
Ayesha Mendonca

Design Lead:
Ella Gallego

Design Assistant:
Jane Armstrong

Marketing Lead:
Sabrina Lipowski

Marketing Assistants:
Lauren Byars, Rachel Hessin & Alexandra Piper

Production Lead:
Jennifer McDowall

Production Assistant:
Lena Schmidt